## Praise for *The*

'An awe-inspiring ability to explo[...]
*Advertiser*

'Johnson is in control as she steers her wonderfully realised characters, and the reader, to a place if not of permanent safety, at least to a landing they can survive.' *Newtown Review of Books*

'Lightness is certainly part of *The Landing*'s appeal, but it is shot through with an equally appealing literary intelligence.' *Sydney Review of Books*

## Praise for *My Hundred Lovers*

'A remarkable achievement, a genuine masterpiece of sensuality and an absorbing and very personal experience, like reading someone's beautifully poetic and honest diary.' *Meanjin*

'The pleasures of bathing, cycling, Paris and song are threaded through memories of unrequited love, unrealised longing and lovers.' *Canberra Times*

'*My Hundred Lovers* is an original imagining of one woman's waning flesh and the vibrant imprint of a life it still holds.' *The Age*

## Praise for *Life in Seven Mistakes*

'She has a knack for presenting what can be unbearable in reality, of rendering it on the page with tremendous heart.' *Sydney Morning Herald*

## Praise for *The Broken Book*

'Both very Australian and resoundingly international, *The Broken Book* confirms Johnson's status as one of the finest Australian writers ... fiercely beautiful.' *The Australian*

'A bold narrative, in which we're constantly reminded by the quality of her prose that this is an imaginative work ... It's a kaleidoscope of memory, jagged and disordered as the artist's tragic life.' *Canberra Times*

## Praise for *A Better Woman*

'I am writing these lines with tears in my eyes ... An extraordinary book from a great writer and a great woman.' Isabel Allende

'Transcendent ... Beautifully written and remarkably wise. A distinguished memoir.' *Kirkus Reviews*

## Praise for *Hungry Ghosts*

'... so well crafted it exudes a breathless quality.' *The Australian*

'An absorbing and disquieting tale of love, friendship, and betrayal.' *Kirkus Reviews*

## Praise for *Flying Lessons*

'Ms Johnson's prose is charged with feeling, insight and rambunctious wit.' *New York Times Book Review*

Susan Johnson has been writing books since 1985, when she received the first of three grants from the Literature Board of the Australia Council which allowed her to write full time. Before that she was a journalist (starting at the *Brisbane Courier-Mail* and going on to work for such diverse publications as *The Australian Women's Weekly*, *The Sun-Herald*, *The Sydney Morning Herald* and *The National Times*).

She's written ten books: eight novels; a memoir, *A Better Woman*; and a non-fiction book, an essay, *On Beauty*. Several of her books have been published in the UK, the US, and in European translation.

She's lived in the UK, France and Greece, but returned to Brisbane, Australia, in 2010. In 2019 she took off again to live on the Greek island of Kythera with her 85-year-old mother, Barbara. A memoir about their adventure is forthcoming.

# SUSAN JOHNSON

# FROM WHERE I FELL

ALLEN&UNWIN
SYDNEY·MELBOURNE·AUCKLAND·LONDON

First published in 2021

Permission to use images on: p. 38 © Anoushka Toronto at Depositphotos, Inc. USA; p. 298 © Anthony Maniaty.

Allen & Unwin
83 Alexander Street
Crows Nest NSW 2065
Australia
Phone: (61 2) 8425 0100
Email: info@allenandunwin.com
Web: www.allenandunwin.com

 A catalogue record for this book is available from the National Library of Australia

ISBN 978 1 76087 655 5

Set in 12/17pt Stempel Garamond by Bookhouse, Sydney
Printed and bound in Australia by Griffin Press, part of Ovato

10 9 8 7 6 5 4 3 2

 The paper in this book is FSC® certified. FSC® promotes environmentally responsible, socially beneficial and economically viable management of the world's forests.

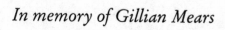

*In memory of Gillian Mears*

For manifestly you have been aware of what
you mean when you use the expression 'being'.
We, however, who used to think we understood it,
have now become perplexed.

PLATO, *THE SOPHIST*

## Raphael

FROM: Pamela Robinson <pamrob@comms.com>
TO: Chris Woods <cwoods@comms.com> <cxwoods@mailsend.com>

Dear Chris,

*Alors*, Raf turned sixteen today. Can you ever forget the sight of him new, no bigger than your fist? A machine keeping his lungs open between breaths, his own body not knowing how to breathe, believing it still lived underwater. Remember when he was released from his radiant cradle I donned a lead apron like a bulletproof vest and placed him against an X-ray machine, holding up his tiny arms, tender as the new shoots of a plant? Why was I wearing the protective vest and not him, his smudge of self, barely there? His lungs were fine and now he is sixteen years old, filling those same brave lungs with carcinogenic smoke. Did you know he smokes? I've forbidden it—of course—but I know he does. The first generation to grow up bombarded with anti-tobacco propaganda and he takes up smoking.

Time is a trickster—I feel at any moment I might turn around and find Raf swaddled on the couch behind me, my first baby, my terror, my love, unfingered by life. Yesterday I came across a photo of him and Claude in the garden at Deauville—before Baptiste was born—both of them small enough to squeeze into nappy buckets, smiling up at the camera. I felt as if I could walk into the frame to find everyone living in that moment, dumb to the future.

I've wanted to write to you many times. Most often to say that if I'd known the cost of leaving the marriage I would never have left. I am to blame for the pain the boys have endured—and if this is something you wanted to hear, then yes, I admit it.

But what I regret most is telling you I didn't love you anymore—bad advice I heeded, and my fault for asking for advice and following it. You will always be the father of my children and I will always love you. For what it's worth, I am very sorry for what happened to us, but sorrier for Raphael, Claude and Baptiste. We created three sons, a truth that will exist forever in time.

Love,
Pamela

## Mistake

FROM: Chris Woods <cxwoods@mailsend.com>

TO: Pamela Robinson <pamrob@comms.com>

Hi Pamela, you have the wrong person/email address. Good luck and hope things work out for you. Take care, Chrisanthi Woods

## Re: Mistake

FROM: Pamela Robinson
TO: Chris Woods

Oh my God, how *excruciating*! I'm not in the habit of pouring my heart out to strangers. My ex-husband (who's Christophe Woods, not Chrisanthi Woods!) has a new email account and I've obviously used the wrong address. Raf showed me an email with his dad's new address but I didn't write it down—I simply assumed Chris changed his old email to the new one, keeping the same address format, so I used both just in case. This one hasn't bounced back, which I suppose means he got my email. He thinks I blew up his life—which I did—just not on purpose like he thinks. He won't speak to me. Oh, dear—I suppose I *do* pour my heart out to strangers . . .

Apologies from Sydney, Australia. Where are you by the way?

Best wishes,

Pamela Robinson

## Hello from Schenectady, New York

FROM: Chris Woods

TO: Pamela Robinson

Hi Pamela, we're in upstate New York. Did you hear back from your ex? Take care, Chris

## Hello again

FROM: Pamela Robinson
TO: Chris Woods

Hi Chris,

I haven't heard a thing.

It feels weird writing an email to someone with the same name as my ex-husband—a Chris who is not 'my' Chris—and a woman not a man to boot. My Chris is Christophe Xavier— what's your X stand for? And you're Chris, not Chrisanthi? I was Pam when I was young, but in my old age I've reclaimed Pamela. My Chris—who's in Paris—only gets Christophe from French people who don't know him.

Best wishes,

Pamela

## Chris or Chrisanthi

FROM: Chris Woods
TO: Pamela Robinson

Hi Pamela, my mom calls me Chrisanthi Xenia (my full name).
Everyone else calls me Chris. PS Your ex should speak to you.
Refusing to speak to someone is usually controlling behaviour.

## Behaviour

FROM: Pamela Robinson
TO: Chris Woods

Hi Chris I Don't Even Know,

Look, I don't know the first thing about you, and you don't know the first thing about me, but aren't some things about everyone the same? Pain is universal, only the details differ, so why does pain feel exasperatingly personal?

I've given up trying to work out other people—how does anyone know anything about anyone? Is my ex-husband's behaviour controlling? He's grievously hurt, that's all—and the older I get, the less I know about anyone. How do we even know pain is universal if we experience it as ours alone? It took me ten years to leave my husband, because I kept seeing things from his point of view and because I kept hoping. We broke up once but I went back because I'm not very good at saying goodbye.

Yours in ignorance,
Pamela

## Re: Behaviour

TO: Pamela Robinson
FROM: Chris Woods

Hey Pamela, you sound like someone who overthinks things. Give yourself a break—take a day off, buy an ice cream. It's summer in Australia, right? When the weather's fine I take my book and my fold-up chair and go sit in the park. Sundays in winter I head to the Dewey. This afternoon two kids came in looking for the library's New Deal murals. You know how kids don't talk these days, they sit with their cell phones, moving their thumbs? So, the girl takes a quick look at the murals, goes straight back to her phone. After a while she asks the boy, without looking up, 'Did you take some photos, Charlie?' And he says, 'Nah. I'll get better ones off Google later on.' What a world. Take care, Chris

**Me again . . .**

FROM: Pamela Robinson
TO: Chris Woods

What do you do in Schenectady? Husband? Girlfriend? Kids? You said 'we' live in Schenectady.

I'm a librarian as it happens (no murals where I work)—I'm fifty-one, headed for the knackers.

Warm wishes,

Pamela

## Knackers

TO: Pamela Robinson
FROM: Chris Woods

Hi Pamela, I'm sixty-four come June so no talk of the knackers please. Right now, I'm looking after a friend five years younger than you, dying of lung cancer, so no complaining either. Kathleen's never smoked in her life, so I was smiling when I read what you said about your son smoking.

Yeah, I've got a husband—Mike. Yesterday he climbed into the trash can to squash down some garbage, the trash can fell over and he cracked his head open. So, now I'm visiting my friend Kathleen in the hospice, my mom in her retirement complex and Mike in Ellis, between driving over to Kathleen's to feed her cat Boris and water her plants. She hangs her dresses according to colour. It's interesting to see the different ways folk live their lives.

I work in Albany, a half-hour drive on a good day, in student enrolments at SUNY. Some days I think it's great, everyone believing their lives will be better than their folks'. When I was young I expected something wonderful would happen to me.

So, a librarian. I'm a big fan of libraries. I'm always reading (I'm an English major). Right now, I'm coming to the end of *Madame Bovary*. This book gives me eyes. I've read it more times than I care to count and whenever I raise my new eyes to the real world I'm a little disappointed. Your ex is French? How come his surname is Woods? Take care, Chris

## Pen pals

FROM: Pamela Robinson
TO: Chris Woods

Hi there,

Isn't this odd, talking to someone you don't know? We're not really talking either—I've got no idea what your voice sounds like or what you look like—although I picture you as tall, with a long, serious face. But really I've got no idea who you are—you could be a twenty-five-year-old Kenyan guy for all I know. It's bizarre—I send an email to bounce off some satellite in space and it falls into your inbox—out of all the Chris X Woodses on the planet who are not my ex-husband. But I'm totally convinced you are who you say you are—I mean, Chris from Schenectady, married to Mike, who climbs into garbage cans. I googled 'M and C Woods, Schenectady' and only a Michael K Woods came up—is that Mike? There are a couple of 'Chrysanthi Woods' on Facebook but no 'Chrisanthi Woods' and none called either in Schenectady. How strange that our lives are so traceable, digital trails everywhere like snails leaving glistening tracks—floating out there in the galaxies.

Once I had another email account—back when email began—and Chris and I courted that way. I mean, we courted in real life, too, when we could. He's American. (Well, he's half French. His mother's French, but his dad was from Detroit, where Chris and his brother grew up, and where we lived for three years after we got married.) I'm 100 per cent mongrel white Australian—a bit of English and Irish, mostly Scots. Chris and I met in New York twenty years ago when I was on the hoof; I've lived a peripatetic life, here and there, everywhere and nowhere. Email was how we kept in touch—our love flung up into the heavens, no letters, no words on paper, only soft words among the planets. A few weeks ago—in the middle of the night, when I couldn't sleep for thinking about how I wrecked everything—I got up and turned on my laptop and logged into an old email service we used. Our emails had vanished—gone! Apparently if you don't use some email addresses after a certain number of years the address evaporates—*pouf*—flung back into the mystery from whence they came. No glistening trails, no comfort for me in the middle of the night trying to warm myself by love's flame. How hard we loved and how dazzling love turned us! Our beautiful words, lost, and only an image left in my head of our love falling back to earth, letter by letter, loosed among the stars . . .

Do you think there are two of us now? Our time is lived in both virtual and physical space, our physical selves and our second selves with our glistening trails, our vanished email selves a kind of cosmic echo. Maybe our virtual selves transmute into a sort of disembodied, captured past, like photographs, a palimpsest of every earlier lost version of ourselves. There I am, a ghost of the air, my younger self eternally in love with my lost Chris, who is not you. And there you are, Chrisanthi Xenia, whose physical self is unknown to me but whom I picture as a tall woman, with a long, serious face. I wish there *were* two of me—I'm too busy to have a pen pal—yet here we are, strangers, connected in air.

Warm wishes,
Pamela

## Re: Pen pals

FROM: Chris Woods
TO: Pamela Robinson

Hi Pamela, yeah, well, here's the one and only me, trying to stop my crazy husband climbing a ladder to paint a wall. Ellis kicked him out after scans showed it was only a hairline fracture. He's Michael W (for Walter) Woods, he ran a radio repair business until everyone stopped buying radios. We're not on Facebook.

I hate to break it to you but I'm not tall. I'm five foot, and carrying too much weight. My face is not long and intelligent. My mother says, 'Kindly show me a pleasant expression, Chrisanthi Xenia, if nature hasn't blessed you with one.' Except she says it in Greek, which doesn't sound so polite.

I had a pen pal back in the day. I was a paid-up member of GOYA (Greek Orthodox Youth of America). Four years straight I wrote my pen pal Dimitra in Athens. I was learning Greek at Saturday Greek school, she was learning English. I wanted to know everything about her: what her room was like, what she ate, did she have a pet. Other people's lives are way more interesting than mine.

Everything was going great until Dimitra got into boys. The closest I got to a boy in those days was watching *The Monkees* on TV. Dimitra was making out with her boyfriend, being wild with other Athenian teenagers. She was in 1969 while I was in 1949, with the other kids whose parents had immigrated to America.

I hope you're a better pen pal than Dimitra. Take care, Chris

## Re: Re: Pen pals

FROM: Pamela Robinson
TO: Chris Woods

Please keep emailing—I promise to be a good pen pal. Lucky for you, I'm never making out with boys again.

    Warmest,

    Pamela

## Update

FROM: Chris Woods
TO: Pamela Robinson

Hi Pamela, so it turns out Kathleen has a sister. She told me she had no family, met her husband Ray on a train, followed him out East. They were married two years when he was electrocuted at work. I was pissed she lied about having no family.

Saturday, I spent the afternoon washing and blow-drying what's left of Kathleen's hair. She likes to keep herself neat. She's dying, and she asks me to pick up some hair combs because hers are broken. 'Could you pick up some hair dye too, please?' she asks, and it was on the tip of my tongue to say, 'What's the point?' when this bedraggled-looking woman walks in, rushes over to Kathleen, cries all over her. I'm about to haul her off when Kathleen mouths, 'No, no, it's OK.' You'd never pick them for sisters.

Jean's her name. She phones Kathleen every couple months on her landline. Kathleen's the only person I know who still has a landline; it kind of goes with her colour-coded clothes. The last time Jean phones Kathleen she can't raise her no matter what time she calls, so she tracks her down to her place of work (she works with me at SUNY) and gets it out of them that Kathleen's in the hospital but not which one. (Stupid new privacy protocols at work meant I couldn't even get the home address of my colleague Tracey when she had another miscarriage and I wanted to visit.) So, Jean rings every hospital across town, gets nowhere, catches a plane from Milwaukee, and takes a cab to every hospital in Schenectady in person. When she can't find her in any of the hospitals, she starts on the hospices until she locates her.

They don't even like each other. Jean's the eldest, and treated Kathleen like she was her personal toy. She cut off Kathleen's eyelashes when Kathleen was eight, and once she made her march (at gunpoint) around the yard on the hottest day of summer until Kathleen fainted. 'It was only an air rifle,' Kathleen says, so I ask her, 'What's the difference between an air rifle and a gun when it comes to shooting a person?' Kathleen shrugs, if lying on your back hardly being able to move counts as a shrug. 'She said if I told Mom she would creep into my room in the night and shoot my toes off.'

Mike is driving me nuts so I've started going to the Dewey evenings as well. I'm the one paying our medical insurance plan and he's the one climbing into trash cans. Sometimes I like living in a book better than I like living my actual life. I think I told you I'm an English major (SUNY, big surprise). I've lived in Schenectady forever. Take care, Chris

## Re: Update

FROM: Pamela Robinson
TO: Chris Woods

Hi again,

I can't tell you how much pleasure your emails bring me—even though we've never laid eyes on each other. How random life is. Look at us: two strangers, accidentally connecting, falling into friendship in mid-air. I admit I still get an occasional queasy moment seeing that 'Chris X Woods' in my inbox, but I'm getting used to it now. It's peculiar having an interaction with someone with the same name, even if it's only a virtual interaction. In a strange way it's like having a second chance at getting it right, if you know what I mean. Don't worry—I'm not some weirdo who's going to turn up on your doorstep, confusing you with him!

And how strange that time exists in two places at once—that you're alive in time in another day, living in another moment. How can it be that you are still in yesterday, and I am alive in today?

Maybe our identities are more fluid now we have multiple virtual versions of ourselves in time. I can assure you I'm me—a librarian of modest means living in a two-bedroom flat the size of a shoebox I'm lucky I could afford to buy, though only with a ginormous mortgage bigger than the flat. It's in a suburb called Ashfield, in the inner west, nowhere near Bondi Beach or the Opera House or any other celebrated Sydney tourist spot. I'm the mother of three boys—two angry teenagers forced to share a bedroom and my littlest, Baptiste, who turned eight last month, aka my let's-try-to-save-our-marriage baby, who sleeps on the enclosed front veranda in a bed he says is too far from mine.

The world needs more people like you—rooted to one spot—than people like me living a helter-skelter life. Can you imagine if everyone were like me, belonging nowhere? Or is it no-one belonging anywhere?

Warmest,

Pamela

## Belonging

FROM: Chris Woods
TO: Pamela Robinson

Hi Pamela, I'll swap you belonging for elsewhere. I'll throw in Mike, who's still climbing ladders. Lucky you, working in a library, surrounded by books. I used to dream of being an American in Paris. I pictured the apartment I lived in, with bookshelves and high windows, opening onto a square. I went to Paris once when I was eighteen. What's your ex-husband doing there? Did you hear back from him?

Kathleen's time is getting close. Waiting for death is like waiting for birth. You know it's soon, you just don't know when. The world seems changed. I go to work, everything looks different. It makes me wonder if any of us are anything more than our bodies. We're all God's creatures, but sometimes I think even He takes His eye off the ball. Take care, Chris

## Elsewhere

FROM: Pamela Robinson
TO: Chris Woods

Hi again,

Of course I didn't hear from Chris! He believes I acted malevolently—that I'm a madwoman who goes around blowing up lives for no good reason. He's in Paris because that's where we lived after we left London (where Raf and Claude were born), which was after Detroit. Chris was the one who wanted to move to Australia. We've lived in so many places, but we've never lived here before, even though the kids are half-Australian. That's when I knew it was over: Chris hoping to find that faultless place where he might find his happiness, only to arrive once more at disappointment—and I couldn't bear the thought of moving again. I couldn't work up the courage to tell Chris it was over until our plans were so well advanced they seemed inevitable. It's like I was a sleepwalker moving towards the cliff, unable to rouse myself. It never occurred to me—not once—that after I told Chris I didn't love him he would choose to stay in Paris while we fell out of our old life into a new one on the other side of the moon. We've been here seven months now.

Chris is never happy, no matter where he is—but I know I'm not the most soothing of companions. I'm not built for moderation. It took me years to understand that most people don't experience rapture lying beneath a frothing pink cherry tree in a spring garden in Deauville, crying for beauty, wanting to eat it—and that most people don't sometimes long to die. In those first weeks when I finally understood Chris loathed me for quitting our marriage—when his hatred caused me to experience myself as putrid, infected—I lay in bed at night, my palms pressed flat beneath my body's weight lest they fly up to my neck and strangle the life from me. The world needs fewer febrile people not lying in beds at night pressing down their self-murdering hands.

I'm sorry about your friend—and I'm ashamed to be talking about longing to die when of course life—as startling and shrouded as it is—is wondrous. It's just that sometimes I'm felled by a feeling that the space in which I live is too cramped for everything I wish to place there. I was once alive on a spring day in Deauville. I hope your friend lived such a moment.

Warmest,
Pamela
X

**(No Subject)**

FROM: Chris Woods
TO: Pamela Robinson


Hi Pamela, I should have been braver. I should have moved to Paris and lived my moment. Without knowing when, I passed the best moment of my life. Take care, Chris

## Sorry . . .

FROM: Pamela Robinson
TO: Chris Woods

Oh, Chris! Sorry for being insensitive—raving on about blossoms and wanting to strangle myself—given your circumstances. But how do you know you have passed your best moment? It might be still to come.

Look, I know you've got painful things to deal with right now. I know, too, that technically we're not friends—but I like to think that we are.

Sending love,
Pamela

## Hello, friend

FROM: Chris Woods
TO: Pamela Robinson

Hi there, Kathleen died. Her sister went home three days before the end, she couldn't wait any longer. It was just Kathleen and me in the room. I asked the nurses for some privacy. They'd been giving her morphine to ease the pain. In truth, I believe they were easing her journey. She stopped speaking the morning before she died. I arranged her hair the way she likes it. Last week I dyed it for her. Chestnut Gold. 'Hair dye,' I was saying as I was putting it on and Kathleen says, 'Hair dye for the dying,' and we laughed the way we used to laugh. 'Your first silver hair is a message from the future,' she says, 'an invitation from the grave.' She starts talking about the lights going out inside her, one by one, raving like someone high on drugs. She sees people in the room: her mother, her husband Ray. She wants to know if I believe anyone will be there to meet her. 'Sure,' I say. 'Sure there will be, honey.' I have my faith, Kathleen lost her Catholic faith as a young woman. Before she got sick she told me she believes pre and post life are the same place, empty, that we come from nothing and return to nothing. In my book it's sad that a woman should die comfortless, believing everyone in the end becomes no-one, from nowhere. Kathleen starts talking about who she wants to see—suddenly she needs to believe in an afterlife again. She doesn't want her mother or her father or her brother Joseph who died when he was twelve. She wants her husband. 'Ray had such clean fingernails,' she says.

When she died, the moment she died, she turned waxy. It was exactly like Hemingway described it at the end of *Farewell to Arms*, when Catherine dies, and Frederic tries to say goodbye. It was like saying goodbye to a statue. I said the prayer Kathleen couldn't say for herself. Take care, Chris

## My condolences

FROM: Pamela Robinson
TO: Chris Woods

Oh, how sad for you—it sounds like you were such good friends. Friends are our witnesses, aren't they, who tell the world who we are—no, they tell *us* who we are. I know I'm impossibly far away—can you at least send your street address, so I can organise flowers? Please, Chris, I'd like to.

Love,
Pamela
X

## Address

FROM: Chris Woods
TO: Pamela Robinson

Hi, don't send flowers. Send a donation to Syria. Saturdays I do free English classes for Literacy Volunteers of America. So, I'm giving an English oral comprehension to recent arrivals from Syria via a Beirut refugee camp—two girls, one shy, silent, the other with blazing eyes and an attitude. The test should be about Dick and Jane going bowling, right? Instead I'm reading from a sheet about a town where the people built an underground city to protect themselves during invasions. Whoever thinks up these damn things hasn't heard of PTSD. So, I'm reading out the oral exam. One question is about why they did it, why the people chose to live beneath the ground. The shy girl says, 'To hide from the bombs.' The girl with the blistering eyes answers, 'To breathe the air of life.'

We are at 70— Hampton Ave, Schenectady, NY 12309. This is so you know I'm a real person, with a home, not for any flowers. Look it up on Google Street View. You can see my neighbour Gene two doors up, his face pixilated, out on the sidewalk, taking a break from fighting with his wife, Patricia. You can see the pool Mike put in that we use maybe two days of the year. People living beneath the earth, us digging it up.

I'm thinking of giving those Syrian kids extra free lessons. But I don't know how I'll find the time between my job, my mom, the house, the shopping, my dog, plus packing up Kathleen's house and trying to find a home for Boris. I do know that you and I and Kathleen and those Syrian girls were born with the exact degree of breath to allow us to breathe the air of life. Take care, Chris

## Life

FROM: Pamela Robinson
TO: Chris Woods

Hi Chris,

What a good person you seem. Whenever I watch programs about a woman opening an orphanage in Africa I immediately want to resign from my job, take my wrecked children, and go and work there—you're the sort of person who would really do it. Will Kathleen's funeral be in Schenectady or in her home state?

Are you the only one dealing with your mother—do you have siblings? Your mother's Greek you said? Is your dad Greek as well? By the way, you never said if you and Mike have kids—so many questions!

I googled your house and saw the pool. How amazing that we can do that now: cross to the other side of the world and see the streets and houses where other people live, while sitting in our own chairs. I felt as if I could walk down the street and knock on your door.

Sometimes I go on Google Street View to look at the apartment where we lived in Paris. Our flat there is old, ghosts in the architecture—it belonged to Chris's late grandmother, in a rundown, mainly North African part of the 19th—but we were lucky, it's on the *rez-de-chaussée* (that's the ground floor) and opens onto a large private garden. On Google I can see the courtyard where we moved the kitchen table every summer. I can pick out the tree I planted with my own hands: a eucalyptus, which is a gum tree native to Australia—a symbol of my homeland in a foreign place. I know what I'm looking for; I'm searching for us, trying to see our faces at the window.

I'm looking for us captured—or lost?—in time. For Raf, before he started to smoke and run outside with his head exploding after yelling obscenities at his brother. There's a war here, except we are not underground. Mercifully, we are physically safe on the surface of the earth, the only bombs are inside our heads. Unlike your poor Syrians, we are in a new country of our own free will, but we are broken too, in undisclosed and more shameful ways. Here we are with our cracked heads . . . what do they call it? A broken family? We are traumatised. Atomised. Exploded.

Chris and I were together twenty years—the muscles of our lives moved together and ripping ourselves apart has left me motionless. It feels so violent, stopping being married to someone. I'm in shock at how fast a lifetime can be undone.

Love,
Pamela
X

## Chestnut Gold

FROM: Chris Woods
TO: Pamela Robinson

Hi, Kathleen's funeral is me and some of the staff from SUNY. The sister doesn't come. Kathleen chose a Catholic church. Go figure. The church is freezing. I keep getting distracted by the ancient priest, who looks like he might drop dead himself. Something's wrong with his voice, like someone with throat cancer who speaks out of that hole in their neck. It's not that, it's not a mechanical sound, it's more like the sound of a teenager whose voice is breaking. This high quivery old voice keeps cracking up—*a time to die, a time to pluck up that which has been planted*—and I all I can think of is how Kathleen would have laughed. I keep looking at the coffin, thinking of her inside, laughing. I read somewhere your hair keeps growing after death. I'm thinking maybe I should have asked the funeral home if I could put in a packet of Chestnut Gold. I'm thinking how the ancient Egyptians used to pack a picnic basket for the journey, how Kathleen could start her travel to the underworld with Chestnut Gold, some colour-coded clothes and maybe Boris's collar. Except the Egyptians would probably kill Boris and pack her in beside Kathleen (Boris is a girl). I kept thinking it should have been an open coffin, so I could see her face. Thank God you're not in Syria. You and your sons are safe and alive. You shouldn't exaggerate. Take care, Chris

## Exaggerating . . .

FROM: Pamela Robinson
TO: Chris Woods

Oh, Chris, sorry *again*. It's hard to be nuanced in emails isn't it—unless you CAPITALISE or use *italics* or exclamation marks!!!! Do I exaggerate? I apologise. These days I'm frequently ashamed of myself—of course I know a family exploded by domestic war does not even begin to compare to the suffering of a people involuntarily expelled from their lives by war. I know, I know! Psychic wars are invisible, fought in air, unless of course pain manifests in the gun or the knife—frankly, I'm surprised there aren't more murderous divorces.

Chris thinks I'm a drama queen—I'm doing a good impersonation of one now, aren't I? I used to write poetry when I was young and for a long time I imagined myself to be a poet—until I showed my work to my adored English teacher. 'It's a bit . . . inflamed,' she said. I never showed my poems to anyone again. Sometimes it seems like I've been watching other people ever since, trying to learn how to be less 'inflamed'. People rush to give me advice—obviously I look like I need it. I do ask people for advice more than other people as well (my best friend Deb says I do and she's usually right), so it's obviously my fault too. There were no boundaries in my family when I was growing up—my father specialised in emotional incontinence. Whatever he felt poured straight from his volatile mouth and, boy, did Papa Robinson feel. Shoot me if I turn out like my father.

It's good to think of you imagining Kathleen laughing—I liked your story about the old priest, too—but, really, you must be full of sorrow. How strange I've grown attached to a woman I've never met living on the other side of the world. You know how on international flights they show the flight path, half the world in darkness, the other in light? These days I often think of the turning earth, of a pearly summer dawn breaking here in Australia—while on the eastern seaboard of America a winter sky stains to black.

I'm at work—my once-a-month late shift—while this lovely young Indian girl Prisha, a uni student, is home looking after the boys. We're about to close, there's a handful of people who've been here most of the day. In summer they come for the air-conditioning, in winter for the heating—people who have fallen through the safety net of life, that web of family and friends and jobs which look ordinary enough on the surface but which underneath bolts together the bones of life. Where do these people go when the doors close and they are cast out into the night? To rooms in boarding houses? To flats in public housing they can't afford to heat when it's cold?

I'm ridiculously busy, too: at work, being the Angel in the House, doing the shopping, cleaning, washing, trying to fit in a regular yoga class, as well as keeping up with the boys' homework, sports events, after-school stuff, not to mention getting them to school on time—every morning is a civil war—all the while trying to make sure they remain safely gathered within that invisible safety net.

I keep forgetting things. Yesterday I forgot a meeting with Claude's head of year—he's struggling with maths and they want to move him to vocational maths, which he says is for dumb kids—and I forgot the meeting until a text arrived and then I had to run down the street to the school like a crazy woman. He had trouble with maths at his old school too—one of Paris's few bilingual state schools, I rush to add, not one of those rich

33

international schools that cost the equivalent of a small African country's GDP. Here in Sydney only expensive private schools offer International Baccalaureate programs—so the older two are at a local boys' high school, which is not proving brilliant. Next, I need to get Raf to an adolescent psychologist—which would mean manhandling an angry six-foot-two man-child into a car. Finally, I need to stop Baptiste sneaking into my bed at night. Is it him or me that needs comforting? Is it too much of an exaggeration to say that holding an armful of warm boy child is my redemption? The remnants of the infant he was—so recently vanished—clinging to his velvety skin. Thank God for children. They puncture everything—pomposity, vanity and ego—and have the miraculous ability to return you to your own body, so that you become nothing more than skin and breath.

I had a dream last night that clung to me all day: everyone's inner selves were rendered visible and some people moved across the earth like flames, flickering, golden—some people *glowed*—but I was this putrefying, blackened thing, low on the ground, washed in shame—the inner me, visible to everyone. I hope that doesn't sound like I'm exaggerating!

I think of you often—I know without setting eyes on you that you're one of those gliding souls who glows.

With love,

Pamela

X

## Gliding . . .

FROM: Chris Woods
TO: Pamela Robinson

Yeah, right, here's me glowing and gliding across to Patricia and Gene's, two houses over, to find Patricia weeping in the cold on the front porch. 'This time I'm going,' she's saying, wiping her nose with her glove. I've lived in Hampton Ave twenty-eight years, and she's been saying that for twenty-eight years. I bite my tongue, because what would happen if everyone went around saying what they really thought? The answer to 'How are you?' would be so long and heartbreaking you would never get to the end.

So, Patricia's weeping in the cold, bitching about Gene. They don't speak to each other; speech is mediated through third parties, schmucks like me or their son Karl, who has insulin-dependent diabetes and lives two streets over. 'He's so passive aggressive,' says Patricia, meaning Gene, not Karl ('passive aggressive' is her favourite term). I know the script by heart: Gene's passive aggressive, hostile to her and the whole of womankind. Gene doesn't have the emotional intelligence to deal with life. Possibly he has Asperger's. Patricia retrained as a marriage counsellor when she was fifty, to give her more weapons to batter Gene with.

'What's he done now?' I ask, trying to keep the weariness out of my voice. Patricia's whining about Gene booking a ticket to California to see his brother who's been diagnosed with Alzheimer's when he knows full well she's due at Ellis for her breast reconstruction on those exact same dates (she had breast cancer). Why pick those exact same dates? I'm thinking:

35

what's it to her where Gene goes or what he does if she hates him? Why is she even a marriage counsellor, a woman with the worst marriage in the world? I'd want my money back if I knew about her and Gene.

'I'm going,' she says. 'As soon as I've recovered. It's over.'

'You can always stay with us,' I say.

She puts a hand on my arm. Looks deep into my eyes. 'You are such a good neighbour, Chris. A really good person.' She's doing that therapist thing. Any minute now she'll talk about boundaries. How I need to keep a wall between myself and other people's needs.

'You do enough,' she says. 'I'm going to Eva's in Brooklyn.' Eva's her best friend, another therapist. They can sit in a room together and bitch about Gene and the emotional stuntedness of men. Then she can move back home again.

Can you see my glow down there in Australia? I'll keep emailing if you promise never to talk about boundaries. Take care, Chris

## In the flesh

FROM: Pamela Robinson
TO: Chris Woods

How I wish I could meet you, Chris! How quickly your emails have become vital to me—I usually save one up to read at lunchtime, or for when I get a quiet moment by myself. But how will we ever know if we really like each other, except by meeting in the flesh? You know how there are some people you dislike on sight? There's this woman at work who has this particular smell—it's not body odour or bad breath or anything as unpleasant as that, it's subtler—but the truth is: I don't like the way she smells. She's not 'my people'. You know that theory you're attracted to people who could be a missing family member? Well, this woman not only doesn't look like my people, she doesn't smell like them either!

What if you and I don't like each other in the flesh? That worries me—inordinately—ridiculously—because I couldn't bear it if we met and disliked each other on sight. What if you don't like the look of me? What if I smell wrong? I'm attaching the most recent photo I could find—when Chris and I had our last weekend away *ensemble*—another last-ditch attempt to save our marriage—a supposedly romantic weekend away alone, the boys packed off to Chris's mother in Deauville. We had a fight straight away—Chris refusing to be in a photograph—so I took a selfie, and he took a photo of me taking a selfie. Of course, I think I'm far more attractive in the flesh (joke)—but I must admit it sort of looks more like me than not. Don't you think beneath the kiss I look angry?

Do you and Mike go off on romantic weekends together? I'd love to know the secret of staying married. Who was it who said that even though no-one knows the virtues marriage requires, she didn't possess them? Do you know marriage's secret virtues?

Answers please to pamrob@comms.com.

With love,

Pamela

X

## Answers

FROM: Chris Woods
TO: Pamela Robinson

What is this? Socrates in suburbia? Your questions are not original. What the hell, here are your answers, which are not original either:

1.   Marriage's secret virtue is knowing you and your husband are in the same story. You both want to be in the story more than you want to be alone. If you want to stay married, don't get divorced is my advice.

2.   Don't marry for love, then spend the rest of your life complaining about love's decline. A husband's a container for the days only. Never expect a husband to be the answer to everything: mind, body, heart, the meaning of life, blah blah blah.

3.   Marriages last because of small acts of self-deception which neither husband nor wife can afford to let themselves admit. Better not think about it.

Take care, Chris

PS We're never going to meet in the flesh so don't worry. I'm never going to send you a photograph.

## Dialogue on the Nature of Love

FROM: Pamela Robinson
TO: Chris Woods

Hi Socrates,

Is that what this is, a Socratic dialogue? A dialogue on the Nature of Love! Great answers, by the way, if cynical (!!!). But, if what you say is true, why do some people want to keep repeating those small acts of self-deception and not others? Why not *everyone*? Surely some people stay committed out of love? Maybe Gene really does love Patricia, and Patricia loves Gene? Isn't that possible? It seems to me, from the outside looking in, that successful long marriages are essentially an intense attachment—an emotional habit so deeply ingrained it's like—I don't know—eating when you're hungry or sleeping when it's dark? But, hey, what would I know?

And—really? Not even a photograph? I suppose Skype or Zoom is completely out of the question then! And do you mean it when you say we're never going to meet in the flesh? I haven't got the money to come right now—my vagrant days are over—but I'm not discounting it—I mean, some day in the future. I just don't want any meeting between us to be too freighted with hope—you know, like some creepy online dating thing when people send photographs of themselves that are twenty years out of date, and the real thing turns out to be balder and much uglier.

I've got to tell you this online dating story, while I'm talking about online meetings versus real ones. I told you about my friend Deb? We've known each other all our lives—we went to primary school together. She's an academic in creative industries—her field is literary theory—and she's totally brilliant. Even though Deb's the same age as me, she had her daughter when she was only a kid herself—she's already a grandmother. Well, she hasn't had a partner for years, despite the fact she also happens to be drop-dead gorgeous (maybe that scares blokes off?). She has this notion that there are fewer men for women like her—like us—who don't list 'exercise/health' as an interest or a hobby, for example. (I don't know what Schenectady's like, but in Sydney there's a whole new race of people running around in exercise clothes as if they're professional athletes training for the Olympics.) She smokes, too. Anyway, I digress . . .

Deb's met a lot of duds—guys who haven't read a book since they finished school—and finally she met this bloke online—a poet, published in serious journals, teaching at a good university outside the city at a place called Armidale in New South Wales. They started to chat first online, then on the phone—good, deep, intelligent conversations that lasted for hours. This went on for months—Deb was nervous about meeting up, in case the reality didn't match the dream. She googled him—*obviously*—and found as many photographs of him as she could. He looked fine—handsome but kind of dishevelled, seen-better-days . . . but haven't we all?

Anyway, she decided to bite the bullet. They arranged for her to travel up by train—she doesn't drive—and to save all the will-we-sleep-together-or-won't-we stuff, he said he had a spare bedroom and she was welcome to stay there. I mean, he said this in advance—to kind of get all that stuff out of the way—and to give them both a loophole if they needed it.

The train pulls up, she takes one look at him, and it's all off. Nothing. He just doesn't do it for her—she knows straight away. What is that? How strange and peculiarly human desire is—so mysterious and yet so specific. He helps her with her bag, he's kind, polite—he just doesn't ignite that flame necessary for love's burn—or even desire's burn. Surely even in your quotidian list of husbandly days, desire must once have blazed? I know the online dating sites now say 'chemistry' takes time, and that arranged marriages can be just as happy—if not happier—than so-called love matches—but Deb didn't want to stick around for the chemistry to develop.

He's cooked a special dinner, got some nice wine, but she wants to skedaddle off to bed as soon as possible. Certainly, he says, because they both know it's not happening—although neither of them says so explicitly—and they say goodnight. She brushes her teeth—she even has her own ensuite, which is nice, he's vacated his bedroom for her and taken the spare room down the hall—and gets into her nightie, when there's a tap on the door. *Shit*, she thinks, *please no*. She doesn't want to have that embarrassing conversation. She wonders if she can pretend to be asleep, but realises she hasn't switched off the light. He'll know she's awake.

'Yes?' she calls through the door.

'I thought you might be cold,' he says. 'I've brought some extra blankets.'

She opens the door. He's got the extra blankets, but he's also taken out his false teeth. HE'S TAKEN OUT HIS FALSE TEETH! She stands there, stunned. You know how old people's faces fall in when they take their teeth out? Well, there he is, holding the blankets, his mouth caved in. She collects herself just in time, thanks him, says goodnight again, and practically slams the door shut in his face. Then she stands there, her back against the door, the blankets in her arms, her heart and head and whole body filled with a kind of racing excitement—or terror—or rage—she doesn't know what—wondering if he were some kind of lunatic.

Do you think he was so enraged by her non-verbal refusal he wanted to scare her? Or punish her? Or maybe it was completely innocent—you know, he took his teeth out before bed as usual and then he remembered that Deb might be cold, so he got up to give her the blankets. What do you think? What kind of man is so comfortable in his own skin—so to speak!—teeth in or teeth out, whatever, it's all the same? I can't work it out—and neither can she—but it's certainly scared her off wanting to take a train to meet any more poets.

Yours, with all my teeth,

Plato

## Teeth

FROM: Chris Woods
TO: Pamela Robinson

Hi Plato, I have my own teeth too. Greeks love to spend money on orthodontic work straightening the teeth of their kids, while fattening them up like prize hogs.

Both my kid sister Theodora (known as Dora) and I spent years with braces and/or retainers.

We have smiles worth a million bucks. Take care, Chris

PS My guess is the poet did it on purpose.

## Re: Teeth

FROM: Pamela Robinson
TO: Chris Woods

Passive aggressive it is then.

**(No subject)**

FROM: Chris Woods
TO: Pamela Robinson

Hi Pamela, I've lost Boris. The roar of Mike's drill (he's replac-
ing tiles in the laundry room), combined with our stupid dog
Mindy, scared her off. Mindy's a short-haired fox terrier, the
breed that shakes all the time, as if you regularly beat them.
She trembles with happiness, fear, excitement. I walk her down
the street, tie her to a post and come out to find a crowd about
to ring the ASPCA. 'She's shaking! Is she OK?'

When I got home from work yesterday Boris raced out
the door as I came in. We spent last night tramping around
in the last of winter's fresh snow taping up lost cat posters. At
2 am I got a call. 'We've got your cat. Do you want to know
what we're doing to her?' They started to tell me before I hung
up. I spent the rest of the night bug-eyed, fuming. For the love
of God, when did this city go to hell in a handcart? Someone
nailed a cat to a tree in Steinmetz Park last year. Mike grew up
a block away from there, when nice families had picnics in the
park on Sundays and boy scouts frolicked in the pond. Back
then the only people in Schenectady with tattoos were sailors
or inmates. What a world. Here's me, lying in bed, typing on
my phone, hoping Kathleen's cat has been hit by a car. Take
care, Chris

## Hell . . .

FROM: Pamela Robinson
TO: Chris Woods

That's awful—what goes on inside the head of someone who wants to cause such distress to another person? I don't mean the psycho who crucified the cat—clearly that's the work of a madman—I mean the person who rings someone in the middle of the night to taunt them? Oh, if only there was a mystical lock on our doors keeping out everything squalid and disgraceful about being alive.

Yours,
Pamela
X

## Being alive

FROM: Chris Woods
TO: Pamela Robinson

Hi there, so I paid $1900 for Kathleen's veterinarian to remove Boris's damaged left hind leg. A car ran her over. The reason she was returned was because I got a tag cut with my cell number the day before she ran off. She was found over in Woodlawn. This nice black family returned her, church people. They insisted on bringing her over themselves, Mr and Mrs Williams. The father makes the kids shake my hand. 'Pleased to meet you,' says the twelve-year-old daughter, who's wearing a plaid skirt and knee socks. *Knee socks*, I kid you not. The son is in his suit and tie. He's the one proudly bearing the bleeding, blanket-wrapped Boris. 'Please, come in,' I say, not yet realising the extent of Boris's injuries. I think it's wonderful these beautiful children are in suits and ties and knee socks. I stop myself telling them one of my good friends at work (Letitia Jones) was the first black female New York State 400-metre hurdles champion. I'm acting like I've never met a black person in my life.

Boris is a mess, bleeding on the kitchen table. Mike comes in, his hair growing out on one side from where the hospital shaved it. Boris starts emitting this wail, eerily human, like the sound of all the world's sadness. 'Shh, shh,' says the son into her ear. 'There now.' It's all I can do to stop myself crying.

So, now Boris is back home from the veterinary clinic, her good hind leg bandaged up and a stump where her other leg used to be. She's like a drunk, lurching around. Even Mindy's steering clear of her after Boris reared up in that way cats do, her back arched like a drawing of a villain cat, hissing. She scratched Mindy's nose, so now Boris is the playground thug, Mindy the intimidated, trembling kid in the corner eating his lunch. We're keeping Boris. Take care, Chris

## Animals

FROM: Pamela Robinson
TO: Chris Woods


Boris is one lucky cat. Guess what? We're an animal household, too! Last Friday I picked Baptiste up from school (I leave work early on Fridays—Prisha picks him up the other days) and instead of doing our usual Friday afternoon treat of a banana smoothie at our favourite cafe, he talked me into dropping into his friend's house. *'Maman! Le chat de Nicky a eu des chatons! Cinq!'* Baps often reverts to French—I'm forever telling him to speak English.

Well, before I knew it, we had a feathery white kitten in a shoebox, being borne through the streets of Ashfield like a prince. His name is Souris.

Overnight Souris has become not just a cat but a symbol, a conduit for unexpressed emotion. I haven't been able to get physically close to Raphael for months—he flinches when I touch him. Occasionally I land a kiss on the back of his neck, darting in and flying off before he swats me away. But last night Raf approached me of his own free will, Souris like a cotton ball in the crook of his arm. 'Look, Mum,' he said. We stood face to face, arm to arm, the sleeping cat between us. I felt the heat of Raf's skin, our blood's history.

And then this morning—in the usual war of getting everyone ready for school—Raf, Claude and Baps had a fight over who was going to feed Souris. 'I'm doing it!' Claude shouted. 'I am!' Raf shouted back, as if they were in kindergarten. Raf and Claude have always fought—possibly because they are only fifteen months apart and Raf, the firstborn, imagined Claude stole the air which was rightfully his. Now they fight non-stop.

They were in the bathroom, manhandling the kitten, Baps was crying, I was shouting—the luckless kitten being pulled in two, as if mauled by dogs. 'Stop! Stop!' I shouted, wrenching the kitten from the boys. 'For God's sake! Behave yourselves!' I settled Souris in his shoebox under the bathroom sink and shooed them out.

Raf and Claude continued fighting in the kitchen—physically wrestling each other now—a brawling tangle of arms, legs, fists and obscenities. I rushed towards them, trying to pull them apart, this seething mass of testosterone and adolescent rage. Our psychic disruption is now manifest—a bodily struggle. Where was the knuckle of male authority to lay down the law? Where was their father?

'Get off me!' Claude shouted, running out of the house. 'You spoil everything!'

Now it's midnight—everyone's asleep. Baps spent the evening dressing Souris in doll's clothes—a sun hat and an apron. I heard him talking, '*Maintenant, mon enfant, nous allons faire un pique-nique en famille.*' A cat is a cat is a cat except when it's not.

Here I am in my kingdom of sad boys, exiled from family picnics. Remind me again why I left my marriage. Why did I destroy the family house? Everyone knows the first law of motherhood is self-sacrifice over self-interest.

Love,
Pamela

### Re: Animals

FROM: Chris Woods
TO: Pamela Robinson

Hi Pamela, Mike and I were on vacation in Florida last summer, driving a hire car across what we thought was a little stream. Except it was deeper than we knew, and the car started getting pushed by water, started tipping over. 'Get out!' Mike screamed. 'Bubs! Get out!' I was already out, running up the road. I didn't even look back. What I'm saying is, I discovered my instinct was not to drown in a river trying to save my husband.

When I was young I wanted to be like Caroline Kennedy, the brave little girl who didn't cry at her father's funeral, who gave her mother a reason to keep living. Today, not so much. Today marks the eighth day in a row I haven't spoken to my self-sacrificing mother. I'm teaching her a lesson. The lesson is: don't be a bitch. Don't say to the daughter who brings you meals, takes you shopping, listens to you complaining about the neighbours and the people coming into the complex banging doors all night, the only person left in Schenectady still talking to you, don't say to her, 'If I had my time over I would never have children.' My mother is a poisonous spider lurking in her cave. I need antivenom. Take care, Chris

## The mystery of mothers

FROM: Pamela Robinson
TO: Chris Woods

Hi again,

Please tell me more about your mother. Mine died three years ago—ten years after my father—but lately I find myself thinking about her more and more. I used to think everything was about my father—violently hating him at the same time as violently loving him—but now I'm thinking more about the mystery of mothers. When Baps comes into my bed, I breathe him in greedily—his little boy smell, his soft feet, his boneless nose. My mother used to say my little brother Scotty was so delicious she could eat him; now I understand what she means. It frightened me as a girl—I suppose on some level I thought it meant the mother consumes the child. But doesn't she? I mean, don't we, us ravenous mothers? If I could eat Baps I would—keeping him safe, un-grown, my unfurled child. That's my terrible instinct—to breathe him in, my last baby, already leaving. Too soon he will outgrow my arms and I too will become the venomous spider lurking in her cave, waiting to snare my lost children.

Yours in truth and horror,

Pamela

X

## Re: The mystery of mothers

FROM: Chris Woods
TO: Pamela Robinson

Believe me, you don't want to know about my venomous mother.
Take care, Chris

## Re: Re: The mystery of mothers

FROM: Pamela Robinson
TO: Chris Woods

I do! I do! My mother's name was Dawn. If she was my beginning she was also a shadow to my father's colossus—I could
never quite see her. I felt only that she didn't like me very
much—she preferred babies and small children, uncorrupted
things, dumb as plants. Something happened to her when she
was a child—some sexual mistreatment, she never spoke of
the details. I only know that very early she formed a distaste
for maleness itself. Once, when she was reading a news report
about a man charged with sexual assault, she announced to
us children over the breakfast table, 'They should cut off his
balls and throw them away.' The fact that she lived with a
man and was the mother of a son must have caused a split in
her—I recognised some buried violence beneath her overly
feminine facade, a terrible conflict between who she was in the
world and who she was, unclothed.

Mum preferred my brother Scotty to me—another contradic-
tion. Scotty was hers in a way I was not. I understand now, as a
mother myself, how one child can be instinctively known, while
another is as alien as a cuckoo. This is possibly motherhood's
greatest secret: a mother is supposed to have no favourite child,
but sometimes her body has already chosen. From the first
Raf was foreign to me—a language I might never learn. He
wouldn't feed, he wouldn't sleep, he would not be comforted.
Whatever it was he needed from me, I could not give him. With
Claude, everything was familiar—he took my breast as if he
had always known it, he stopped crying the instant I picked

him up. Baps, too, I knew instinctively—and now, of course, I wonder if all Raf's woes don't stem from our first bodily misunderstanding. But do I love him any less? I do not. In fact, because our connection is so hard won, I possibly love him too much. More than the other two, Raf's the child who needs my love most.

Love,

Pamela

X

## People

FROM: Chris Woods
TO: Pamela Robinson

Hi Pamela, Dora is Mom's favourite. The daughter who needs to be reminded it's her mother's birthday. The daughter who never sees her mother. Dora is Mom's brag card when she's out visiting. 'My other daughter, Theodora, lives in the city. She's a partner in one of New York's biggest law firms. Did I tell you?' Mom's name is Calliope. Mrs Calliope Pappas and don't forget it.

So, today Patricia phones to ask me to get Gene to change the dates he's flying to California to see his brother. She's still at Eva's in Brooklyn, not talking to Gene. Gene's still not talking to Patricia. I'm thinking: is this a comedy script? Is there a hidden camera like on *Candid Camera*? Did you get that show over in Australia? I loved it when I was a kid. A hundred-buck note glued to the pavement and some idiot trying to pick it up. Like everyone else, I believed other people were the idiots and not me.

Picture it. Me with Gene on his evening walk, puffing like a steam train. I'm being pulled along by my trembling dog, who has never learned to walk on a leash. Gene's one of these guys who wants everyone to know he's still got it. He walks fast, too fast for me. He's got a gym in the basement, where he lifts weights and runs for miles on his running machine. One day I will sneak up behind him while he's on it and whisper: 'You're still going to die, Gene.'

Maybe I'm a bitch like my mother.

'So, Gene,' I say, 'Patricia wants to know why you can't change your ticket to LA.'

'Because I can't,' he says.

'Come on,' I say, 'she's due at Ellis those exact same dates. Can't you fly out the following week?'

'No,' he says.

'You want me to get Karl to talk to you?' Karl is their son, the one with diabetes a few streets over.

'No,' he says.

'You did it on purpose, right?'

'Yes,' he says.

By now I'm puffing so hard I can hardly talk. 'Can we slow down?'

He looks at me, like he's just noticed I'm there. 'You're carrying too much weight, Christine. You need to lose fifteen pounds. Maybe twenty.'

'My name's not Christine,' I say, 'and mind your own goddamn business. You think I don't know I need to lose weight?'

'How should I know?' he says. 'If you know already, why don't you lose weight?'

I stop walking. 'Are you serious? You, Gene Bennett, having the nerve to tell me if I know something I should act? You, who's lived thirty years in the same house with someone you hate?'

He starts walking. 'Who says I hate her? She's my wife.'

I start walking again. 'Then if you don't hate her, change your ticket,' I say.

'Yeah,' he says, 'and if you know you're fat, lose some weight.'

People, huh. Take care, Chris

## Re: People

FROM: Pamela Robinson
TO: Chris Woods

Hi Chris,

Can we come and live on your street? It sounds so much more fun than ours. I've turned into someone who's embarrassed to run into the neighbours. I'm forever screaming, *For God's sake, stop fighting! Don't leave the fridge door open! Can you PLEASE pick up your clothes? Raf, have you been smoking again? TURN OFF THAT COMPUTER NOW! HOW MANY TIMES DO I HAVE TO TELL YOU?* I hate the sound of my own voice. How did I ever think having small children was difficult? I was their ruler, my body their kingdom—their whole selves turned to me like plants to the sun.

When I was pregnant with Raf we lived in a block of flats. In the apartment next to ours there was a stressed single mother with a toddler. I used to run into her in the street, pushing her pram, looking harassed—her son was always crying, his mouth open in a permanent howl. We heard him crying through the walls at night, every night. 'Do you think he's OK?' I asked Chris. 'It doesn't sound normal.' I was so smug, with my pregnant belly, my unborn child so perfectly behaved. I read somewhere you can keep imagining you're a nice person until you have children. Who knew having children revealed your true nature—that I was so weak, so wanting?

Now I'm that single mother. Is the opposite of a single mother a double mother?

Love,

Pamela

## Re: Re: People

FROM: Chris Woods
TO: Pamela Robinson

Hi Pamela, depends on the mother. In Greek mythology *Εχιδνα* is half-mother, half-snake, which kind of sounds like Mom. Only difference is *Εχιδνα* lived alone in a cave rather than in a retirement community called St Sophia's. Take care, Chris

**(No subject)**

FROM: Pamela Robinson
TO: Chris Woods

Hi Chris,

Well, the shit's hit the fan. Last night the cops brought Raf home—he was busted painting graffiti on an overpass above the highway, and they've charged him with damaging public property. He had two cans of spray paint in his backpack—it turns out he's been climbing out his window at night for months.

The cops banged on the door so hard they must have woken the whole block. I opened it in my gaping dressing-gown—I couldn't find the cord to tie it up—Claude wild-eyed and Baptiste, howling, clinging to my waist.

There were two of them, one either side of Raf, who stood at the front door with his eyes down. They told me what happened, then marched him inside—the shorter, younger cop sat down and made Raf sit opposite. 'OK, let's start at the top, mate. You know a criminal record makes it harder for you to get a job, travel overseas or rent a flat.' Raf kept his head down. 'Do you want to start your adult life like that, Raphael?'

If I saw Raf coming down the street on a dark night, I'd cross the road. He's shaved off his beautiful blond curls—he looks like a racist skinhead, a paid-up member of the National Front. He's got three studs up one ear—he takes them out every morning before school. Mostly you can't see Raf's head because he wears a hoodie. If he's not wearing a hoodie he's wearing a baseball cap back to front—like he's an LA gang member instead of a middle-class teenager with a mother and father who aren't criminals or drug-users and who never in their whole lives abused him, sexually or otherwise. We kept him close! We kept him over our hearts—Chris walking night after night around Greenwich, Raf in a pouch, breathing over Chris's heart—an extension of our love, a physical manifestation of it alive in the world. Raf's head as round as an orange in my hand, his breath unsullied air and breast milk. What have we done to him?

I looked across at his emerging adult face—his future breaking through, his features too large, the bright flare of pimples across his cheeks. He wouldn't meet my eyes.

The young cop was telling him this was his best chance, the wake-up call he needed, life biting him on the bum.

'Can you respond, please, mate?' the cop asked.

Raf didn't speak.

'Come on, mate. You need to look me in the eye like a man.'

If he called him 'mate' again I was going to clock him. 'Mate' is what's wrong with this fucking country.

Raf didn't raise his head but sort of looked up, his brow furrowed. If you can look at someone through your eyebrows, that's what he did.

'In the Children's Court you'll probably get a good behaviour bond. Because it's your first offence, no criminal offence will be recorded,' he said. 'But if you offend again you won't be so lucky. Do you understand?'

Raf nodded.

'Can I hear you say it, please?'

'Yes,' Raf mumbled.

'Yes?' He had his hand cupped to his ear theatrically.

'Yes, I understand,' Raf said.

'Good luck, mate,' the cop said. 'This is the moment when you can change your life for the better.'

He stood up to go and the older cop—who had never sat down—motioned with his head that I should follow them out. 'Any father around?' he asked at the door.

'In Paris,' I said.

He wrote this down in his little notebook. I felt like I was going to be charged too, I don't know with what. For being divorced? For living a vagrant life which confused our defenceless children, not knowing if they are French, American or Australian? For one panicked moment I thought the cop might take my kids away—charge me with negligence—for not knowing I had a son climbing overpasses at night, endangering his life by dangling over bridges.

I'm sorry if this sounds like I'm exaggerating.

Love,

Pamela

## Raphael

FROM: Chris Woods
TO: Pamela Robinson

Hi Pamela, Raf sounds like one troubled kid. Can you get him to talk to someone? Someone who's not you? His mother is the last person he wants to talk to right now. Take care, Chris

## Re: Raphael

FROM: Pamela Robinson
TO: Chris Woods

Hi again,

What if I'm always the last person Raphael wants to talk to? I keep seeing his face from one awful day when he was about a year old—we were living in London and I was heavily pregnant with Claude when the muscles of my lower back split, and a doctor ordered bed rest. I didn't have any relatives to look after Raf, so I spent days interviewing various local carers until at last I agonisingly picked one. The woman was a registered carer, but she was a stranger! I left him screaming his heart out at some unknown woman's door while I walked away. Guilt lodged in my throat as I walked, fast—almost running—but you know what my shame was? My guilt was mixed with a great streak of relief that I was free of him.

Here's the truth—I never fully surrendered to motherhood. I can feel it in my body even now—that feeling of enlargement as I walked away, of being able to expand back into my full shape in the world as if I'd been confined in a box. Maybe that's what your mother was clumsily trying to say when she said she should never have had children. In leaving my marriage I chose my happiness over theirs—in some unpardonable way I became the anti-mother.

Love,

Pamela

## Re: Re: Raphael

FROM: Chris Woods
TO: Pamela Robinson

For Christ's sake, Pamela, why did you have children if you weren't prepared to surrender? Everyone says people who don't have children are selfish. I think it's people having children for no good reason who are the selfish ones. I'm not sure we should keep emailing each other. My heart is banging so hard I feel like I'm having a heart attack. This isn't good for me. Bye, Pamela.

## Re: Re: Re: Raphael

FROM: Pamela Robinson
TO: Chris Woods

Chris, I'm so sorry! I'm mortified I've distressed you—I burst into tears when I read your email. I shouldn't have spoken about my feelings about my sons without knowing your personal circumstances. Please, tell me what I can say to make it up to you. Will it make things worse if I tell you that although I said I should never have had children, I couldn't bear the thought of living without them?

Can you forgive me? I've come to look forward to your emails so much. I don't go around spilling my guts to everyone, which is why our exchanges have become so vital to me so quickly— email as a kind of virtual confession box in the anonymity of space—all my worst stories inside. But I also hoped—or dared believe—that our emails meant something to *you*. I thought you might see them as I do—as a sort of pressure valve in which to release the struggles of daily life, a modest vehicle for sorting through some of life's chaos.

Will you please reconsider? Tell me about not having children—or maybe you *do* have children? I don't know—I don't want to upset you any further. I don't know anything these days, except that your emails are a splash of joy in difficult days—and that I'm a fool who is begging your forgiveness.

With apologies, and love,

Your friend,

Pamela

X

## I'll think about it

FROM: Chris Woods
TO: Pamela Robinson


I'll think about it. That's all I want to say right now. Take care, Chris

## Love's house

FROM: Pamela Robinson
TO: Chris Woods

Hi Chris,

I haven't contacted you in a while—basically because I don't want to aggravate you even further—but I miss your emails. I'm really hoping you'll decide to start emailing me once more. In the meantime, can I tell you what happened to Raphael? Please never think I don't love him—never think that!

He wore his suit to court—the pink tips of his ears looked impossibly naked without his hoodie. He looked about twelve. Heartbreakingly, he'd sprayed on too much deodorant—the more he sweated, the more this dreadful chemical scent rose. Before our appearance we had to wait in a kind of holding pen—the mothers and wives and sisters and girlfriends dressed like they were going to the beach, the boys and men due in court squeezed into ill-fitting suits like overstuffed sausages. I thought of my parents and how ashamed they would be. My father used to call such people 'low-lifes', even when his own drug-taking son—my late brother Scotty—joined their ranks. That's us these days—the hapless single mother with her troubled kids running amok. How could I not have known Raf was sneaking out at night? How did we fall so fast from our lives, as surely as your Syrian girls, but without the excuse of bombs?

The magistrate was a woman, younger than me. My son, in court! The sight of Raf standing there, his head bowed, caused me for a terrible moment to think I might faint. I am by nature intimidated by authority—inexplicably scared when I approach passport control that I will be refused entry because of some unknown but fatal misdemeanour. My heart thrashed—even though our lawyer explained that Raf is a juvenile and would be treated as such—and I feared at any moment he might be hauled off to the cells.

'I trust you appreciate the seriousness of this offence, Raphael,' the magistrate said. 'Repairs to public infrastructure vandalised by graffiti is costing the public purse millions of dollars. Sydneysiders are sick of it.'

Raf kept his head bowed.

'We are a city that embraces street art and public murals, but we are also committed to putting a stop to graffiti defacing public property. On the night of March 29, you wilfully damaged property belonging to the people of New South Wales. Police caught you in the act of painting what is known as your tag. Moreover, police have in their possession images of you captured on CCTV.'

I half expected Chris to burst into court at the last minute, like in one of those American TV shows—I've emailed him, sent him court documentation, but heard nothing back. I know he's talking to Raf—I heard them yesterday on the phone—but Raf won't talk to me, we no longer speak the same dialect. Forget French or English, no language on earth synchronises our tongues and hearts now.

The magistrate went on about Raf's arrival in Australia—asking if his mother tongue was English or French—telling him to speak up and to look at her when he spoke. Raf suddenly looked frightened, as if he might cry—I wanted to leap from my seat and yell, *Stop! You have no idea what he's been through, his family wrecked, his old life vanished!* It seemed incredible to me that I couldn't rush up and bundle him out—out of the room, the building, out of this terrible new life. It was me and not him who should be judged, found unfit. I was the one who broke love's vow, who failed to protect Raf from love's dismantling.

Anyway, he got off. As a first-time offender, he was handed a twelve-month good behaviour bond. No conviction was recorded.

I hope one day he forgives me for being flawed, and partial—for not defending love's house and keeping him forever safe inside.

With love,
Pamela

## Are you there?

FROM: Pamela Robinson
TO: Chris Woods

Hi Chris,
Just wondering if you've forgiven me. I miss your emails.
With love,
Pamela

## (No subject)

FROM: Pamela Robinson
TO: Chris Woods

Hi Chris,

Do you know why my husband won't speak to me? Because he believed I was a fellow traveller in his plans to move to Australia, but—unforgivably—I was not. I was unhappy for years and years—pick from the marital smorgasbord of discontent. We got to a point where we had opposing views on everything. Raf once said to us, 'I don't know why you two bother arguing. You're exactly the same.' We'd separated once before—before Baps was born—but this time whenever I tried to talk to Chris about how we might part with as little disruption as possible for the boys his response was, 'If you want to go, go. I'm not leaving this time.' The last time I said our marriage was over, Chris was the one who volunteered to move out.

But how could I walk out and leave my children? And—if I couldn't leave them—how could I smuggle them out of our flat while Chris was not home, like figures in a Victorian melodrama? I sought help from a top Paris divorce *avocat*, who advised me to inform my husband I no longer loved him and change the locks. But I couldn't lock my own husband out of his home! The husband I could not hate, no matter how unhappy I was; whom I pitiably and doggedly continued to love in all his wounded humanity.

I'm a coward. I followed the *avocat*'s advice and told Chris I no longer loved him but I did it over the phone—I didn't trust myself to say it in person. I said those terrible words while I was away with the boys, saying goodbye to friends, just weeks before we were due to leave for Australia. Chris was in Paris at the hotel where we were staying, finalising a few things—he'd left his job, our flat was rented out, I was due to start my new job here in the library. Our whole lives were packed up—we were at the point of no return. But I suddenly found I couldn't bear the thought of carrying our unhappiness somewhere else. I couldn't bear setting up another miserable home, and finding everything in the exact same place. Of course I should have told him sooner! My timing was appalling—unconscionable—which is why he won't speak to me. He kept asking me to repeat what I was saying, as if he could not hear me properly, as if he could not allow the meaning of my words to reach his ears, much less his understanding. I was telling him his life was over. I pictured his face—have I told you about Chris's face? How he looks like an Italian saint?

With love,

Pamela

## The Fake Grass House

FROM: Pamela Robinson

TO: Chris Woods

Hello,

Me again. I'm the Scheherazade of the internet—telling you stories to keep myself alive.

Tell me what you think of this one. You know we live in a tiny flat—all I could afford after we divided our financial assets. I suggested Chris buy me out of the apartment in Paris for a modest sum so we could settle things quickly and didn't have to spend the next hundred years in a French court. I had no idea that when Chris finally understood that this time I meant our marriage was truly over, he would throw up his hands and let us walk away. I thought he would fight for custody tooth and nail—but, if my fears were apocalyptic, they did not extend to imagining Chris's grief would cause him such agony he might prefer for us to live on the far side of the world so that he never had to lay eyes on us.

There are lots of blocks of flats around Ashfield where we live, and streets of dark brick houses. A lot of the houses are owned—or were owned—by migrants who came to Australia after the Second World War—Italians and Greeks—so sometimes you still see front gardens turned into vegetable patches. But there's this one house a few streets away from us which doesn't have a vegetable patch or a traditional garden or even the slab of concrete you sometimes see in place of a lawn—it has *fake grass*.

The fake grass doesn't just cover their entire front garden—a sea of clever camouflage plastic—it covers the footpath up to the gutter outside the house too. It looks *so* weird—and this fake grass has now become the only neutral topic of conversation between Raf and me, and between the boys themselves, without getting anyone into an argument.

I offer to drive the boys everywhere so we can drive past the Fake Grass House—the four of us in the car, not looking at each other, facing straight ahead, talking. I drive Claude to maths tutoring—I drive both the older boys to soccer training and matches—I drive everyone around more than I should. Sometimes I drive with Raf in companionable silence to meet his friends—he's not allowed out at night so it's only during the day—and I'm reminded of those early days when he was a baby and I spent my days driving around London because a moving car was the only place he would sleep.

I paid a locksmith to put a lock on the boys' bedroom window—then I had to buy a fan because Raf and Claude complained about having no air. If home is a prison, a car is our release.

Every time I drive past the Fake Grass House I say, 'I wonder if today's the day we'll see the people who own the fake grass. Then we'll finally know what they look like.'

Claude thinks they'll be a young Chinese couple with allergies. I suggest it's an Italian man whose wife died long ago and who has grown too old to mow. Raf thinks it's a single guy with OCD who lives alone and keeps surfaces in his house free of clutter—a control bot. I say perhaps it's a family with boys kicking footballs, 'Remember Marcel's garden? His parents laid down new lawn three times before they gave up and put in fake grass because Marcel and his brothers kept destroying it.' But, of course, that was the *back* lawn, which couldn't be seen. What kind of person lays fake lawn out the *front*?

This morning I drove Raf and Claude to school—I'd walked Baps to his school earlier—and we were running late because of last-minute homework. I said my usual thing as we passed the Fake Grass House, wondering whether today was the day when we'd see the people who owned the fake grass. Raf, who was in the back, said, 'I hope we never see them, because then we can keep imagining who they are.'

Pamela

X

## The other side of the world

FROM: Pamela Robinson
TO: Chris Woods

Hi Chris,

Here's a story I'm hoping you might like. Sort of the opposite to your neighbour Patricia, in a way. I have this friend—not a close friend, someone I knew years ago at university—well, I ran into her yesterday. We spontaneously decided to have coffee since we knew if we exchanged numbers we would never see each other.

She told me that one day, out of the blue, her mother announced she was leaving Australia for New York. Her mother had seven daughters—including my friend—and she was a widow, a woman who had never worked since her marriage to a farmer forty years before. But now the farmer was dead, her daughters were grown, and she was moving to New York. She had been a schoolteacher, long ago, before her marriage, and she dusted off this ancient qualification and took off.

I don't know how (she didn't even have a green card), but she got herself a job in a rough school in the public system, and a one-room apartment—in Queens, I believe. They loved her, this old Australian woman arrived from nowhere. Not *old* old—she was sixty-five, I think—I mean too old to suddenly change your whole life by moving to New York.

I love this story. I like to think of the widow at her dirty window in a small room in Queens, looking happily out at the snow, her husband dead, her seven daughters on the other side of the world.

With love,
Pamela

**Life . . .**

FROM: Pamela Robinson
TO: Chris Woods

Hi again,

Persistent, aren't I? I suffer from that female curse—I want people to like me. Even invisible women I've never met on the other side of the earth.

Can I tell you about something I read at work the other day? I often read the science and medical journals we keep in the collection—all the strangeness about being alive is in them. There was a paper by a neurologist in Europe somewhere—Spain or Portugal, I think—reporting the case of a sixty-year-old woman who, following a stroke, completely lost the concept of 'mine'.

Her house didn't feel like hers, her furniture, her dog— even her own husband. She saw them all right, she recognised them, they weren't unfamiliar to her—she had simply lost her sense of ownership over them—meaning she lost her personal history of the world, the physical trail of things to which she was previously attached, and which we believe makes us who we are. She didn't care about the earrings bequeathed to her by her dead mother, she didn't care about photographs from her childhood—the clutter and debris of a life that was previously hers. 'My' house is believed to be a sort of extension of personality, isn't it? A representation of character—the 'me' who prefers antiques, say, to cubical modern furniture, or the 'me' who is married to a handsome architect who wears cool clothes rather than an obese truck driver in a singlet. Ownership implies choice—that you have chosen this over that—that you have claimed something as yours. Yet losing this feeling of 'mine'—which is perhaps another word for 'home'—didn't make this woman unhappy. On the contrary, she said she felt suddenly free.

With love,
Pamela
X

**(No subject)**

FROM: Pamela Robinson
TO: Chris Woods

Hi Chris,

I can no longer control my own children—there, I've said it.

I can't stop Raf and Claude playing Xbox or spending hours on their phones. Every night ends in fights and swearing—I want them off the Xbox or I ask them to put down their phones, but they ignore me until I unplug the modem or wrest their phones from their hands, then doors are slammed, obscenities are shouted.

I can't stop Raf storming into my room after I've hidden the modem—flicking on the light switch and standing over me, shouting at me to give him the modem back as I cower in bed—then ransacking the bedroom until he finds it.

I can't stop him leaving the flat at night—a condition of his good behaviour bond. He walks out the front door whenever he wants to—he has burst out of the architecture, too vast for the frame.

My authority as a parent has flown out the fucking window.

Pamela

X

## A dream

FROM: Pamela Robinson
TO: Chris Woods

Dear Chris,

Here I am—still hoping I haven't hurt your feelings so much that you never want to email me again.

For years I had this dream, a very particular dream, over and over. There were trees—ghost gums—a horizon, with oddly shaped clouds. It was Australia—but nowhere I recognised.

Then, on the day of my father's funeral, I was in the back of a funeral procession car with my mother, following the hearse, when I looked out the window. I saw the landscape from my dream.

With love,

Pamela

X

## Re: A dream

FROM: Chris Woods
TO: Pamela Robinson

Don't you get sick of talking about yourself all the time?

## OK

FROM: Pamela Robinson
TO: Chris Woods

OK, I get it—I *finally* get it. It's over—whatever 'it' was. I wish you all the best.

Pamela

## Sorry

FROM: Chris Woods
TO: Pamela Robinson

That was mean. You caught me on a bad day. Take care, Chris

## Starting again

FROM: Pamela Robinson
TO: Chris Woods

Hi Chris,

You know how women are always being told not to say 'sorry'? Well, how about your sorry cancels my sorry and there's no sorry left to say? Let's just say apologies universally accepted—and start again.

Tell me what's been happening with *you*.

With love,

Pamela

X

## Muaz and Zahiya

FROM: Chris Woods

TO: Pamela Robinson

Hi Pamela, same old, same old. Spring's arrived. The summer clothes are down from the loft. Every spring I go through them and donate to charity everything we didn't wear last summer. I don't go through the clothes *before* I pack them because I don't like summer's passing. I stash everything away real quick, like if I do it fast enough it's not really happening.

I'm giving free lessons to those two girls I mentioned, Muaz and Zahiya. Turns out they're non-identical twins. Muaz is the firecracker. She says as soon as she can she's going back to fight for her country. 'I was on fire but in America I am drowning,' she says. I tell her she shouldn't be in a hurry to jump back into the flames. The girls and their mom spent two and a half years in a refugee camp in Beirut before they were classified for resettlement. Their father disappeared.

Muaz drapes a Syrian flag across her backpack for school, the flag used by the Syrian opposition, and her backpack is covered in *I Love Syria* stickers. She gets into fights. She wants me to know what her old life in Raqqa was like, hearing their father had been arrested, sitting in the dark without electricity, leaving everything behind. 'We walked out of our lives,' she says. 'My mother gave our house keys to our neighbours. She told them, "Our house is yours."'

To Muaz, nothing in America is the right shape. The trees are not the right trees, our spring is not the right spring, food does not have the right flavour in her mouth. 'The birds are wrong,' she says.

Last week she got into a fight with another Syrian girl at the hostel where they're staying. The other girl said the Assad flag is the true flag of Syria. Muaz said the revolutionary flag from the Free Syrian Army is the true flag. The lengths people go to trying to prove they are different from other people. Everyone's the same in their graves. Take care, Chris

## Re: Muaz and Zahiya

FROM: Pamela Robinson
TO: Chris Woods

Hi there,

Oh, Chris, I'm *so* pleased to hear from you! I can't tell you how happy your email made me—a charge of joy straight to the heart. I've missed your stories—even sad stories about girls walking out of their lives.

With love,
Pamela
X

## As the angels fly

FROM: Chris Woods
TO: Pamela Robinson

Hi Pamela, listen, honey, people have been walking out of their lives forever. Syrians, the Irish, Jews, Christians, the men and boys of my mother's village in Greece, marched from their beds in the middle of the night by the Germans and shot on a hillside. Mom's fifteen-year-old brother Angelo was the only male in the house. Their father died five years before.

After the men and boys were killed there was no-one left to bury them. The priests were dead, too. Sometimes I feel so sorry for my mother I forgive her everything. The next moment I'm so angry with her I can't get away quick enough.

My grandmother, my *γιαγιά*, told me that when I was born Angelo's spirit flew over the sea from Kalavryta and landed in my eyes. Yiayia measured distance 'as the angels fly', so that Albany is approximately twenty miles from Schenectady as the angels fly.

Muaz is as far from home as the angels fly. Everyone is far from where the angels fly. Take care, Chris

## Re: As the angels fly

FROM: Pamela Robinson
TO: Chris Woods

Hello Chris,

What does it look like being far from the angels? Like a young man with a shaved head, smoking in the dark. Raf's sitting out the front now, cross-legged on a brick wall built by a homesick Italian.

Being far from the angels means being filled with dumb love, secretly watching your son from a window. If only we could fully reveal ourselves. If only we could heave our hearts to our mouths.

With thankfulness for your friendship,

Pamela

X

## Dialogue on the Nature of Revealing Ourselves

FROM: Chris Woods
TO: Pamela Robinson

Dear Plato,

1.   You know what civilisation is, right? It's passing out of childhood, where you stare at anyone different, gang up on people you don't like, and say whatever you like. Adulthood is *not* revealing ourselves. Imagine if everyone went around being kids again. You know what happened in *Lord of the Flies.* I was a fat kid and every morning on the way to school I threw away my lunch of λουκούμι and cream cheese sandwiches (no one loves Philly like the Greeks). One morning my mother followed me and ordered me to get my lunch out of the trash and eat it in front of her. The kids at school called me Blubber Guts.

2.   America's gone to the dogs because everyone reveals themselves. Do I need to know some Kardashian is fighting with her husband? I do not. Do I care if some crackhead is screaming at his neighbour over the rent on *Judge Judy*? I do not. Keeping some things left unsaid is my preference.

Take care, Socrates

## Our true hearts

FROM: Pamela Robinson
TO: Chris Woods

Hi again,

But Chris, seriously, wouldn't it be better if everyone knew everyone else's true hearts? Our fears and intentions and motivations are so obscured from one another—much less from ourselves—we are but the tiniest outcrop of visible rocks on the surface of a boundless sea.

Whenever I think about my marriage, I imagine only the things I couldn't see. The wounds, the fears—it seems to me we were eternally fighting over something nameless and inexpressible, and never over the particular 'thing' we professed to be fighting about. We were fighting to be heard, for agency, for independence or sovereignty, for something undefined and longed for, denied to us as children. Was I fighting my husband, or my father? I fought the same fight, over and over.

I should have been kinder—I should have loved harder. I should have understood Chris felt under pressure about money. He's a really talented graphic designer—he gets jobs anywhere—but I couldn't get work in Paris as a librarian. My French wasn't good enough—like any unskilled immigrant I did piecework, except I wasn't working on a sewing machine, I was getting 10 euros an hour teaching English to kids who didn't want to be there. Why didn't I see that Chris feeling stressed about money was about fear—which manifested in him being bad-tempered and liable to pick fights? Why wasn't I slower and calmer—a more soothing presence—rather than

93

the inflamed person I am? Love is a practice—anyone can love anyone if they practise hard enough.

Yours in love and friendship,

Pamela

X

## Re: Our true hearts

FROM: Chris Woods
TO: Pamela Robinson

Hi Pamela, no offence, but sometimes you go on with a lot of baloney. Sometimes two people just don't get along. End of story. The part I don't get is why two people who don't get along stick around each other. You should come meet Patricia and Gene. Take care, Chris

## Re: Re: Our true hearts

FROM: Pamela Robinson
TO: Chris Woods

Hi Chris,

Ha! Where could I have possibly got my Old Testament idea that marriage is for life and divorce is for losers? The sanctity of the family is one of the central shrines of Christianity, of conservatives everywhere—the Nazis were especially good at extolling the virtues of marriage and the family. Marriage is the battering ram of the bourgeoisie! My template comes not only from the culture in which I live, but my parents' marriage—of course!—where being able to say with pride *we were married for fifty-five years* triumphed over everything. I once saw my mother punch my father in the side of the head, because he had drunk too much—as usual—and because he was going on and on about whatever he was going on and on about and she had politely asked him to stop too many times. But this was at the end of their marriage—not long before he got sick—when the anger she had concealed for most of her married life was unsheathed.

More usually, my father went on and on without the punch. His verbal bullying reached every corner of the house, running up the walls and out the windows, lectures which turned into rants, words which turned into guns. If my instinct was to run away, my brother Scotty's was to try to win his respect. But how can anyone win the endorsement of a man who wishes the approval of the world to land only on himself?

My father obliterated all comers—friends, colleagues, secretaries, his children—and most certainly his wife. Yet my mother clung to the idea of her successful marriage all her life. Her success was winning him, a man who ensured she need never work again, who guaranteed she would always travel first class. He stalked the earth while she eased his days—even in the final hours of his long, slow death when I was home from Paris to help. She and I stood either side of his hospital bed, fulfilling his commands for water, for another illegitimate sleeping pill, for a large dash of overproof rum in the glass of Coke he drank with a straw every night till the end. In the days immediately after he died—after we followed the hearse and I saw the landscape from my dream—my mother broke down. She turned to me and said, 'I sat with him day after day, Pamela. Not once did he ask if I was going to be all right. Not once did he wonder what was going to happen to me.'

It was the only time she admitted my father's failings. After that, the surface closed over, and for the rest of her life she told everyone with pride *we were married for fifty-five years*. It didn't matter to her what bad behaviour, insults or lack of kindness those fifty-five years contained, because any marriage—a dead marriage or an empty marriage or a bad marriage—triumphed over a broken one. And who among us doesn't long for a happy ending?

But what did it stand for, that victorious flag pitched at the top? My mother might have said it stood for loyalty, endurance, a pledge—most likely she would have declared the flag stood for love. For all I know, she was right.

Yours in bafflement,

Pamela

X

## Bad news

FROM: Chris Woods

TO: Pamela Robinson

Hi Pamela, I've got bad news. Gene died. A heart attack. It was me who found him, when I was out walking Mindy. He collapsed on the pavement a couple streets over.

I'm staying at Patricia's. I've moved in to cook, clean, help etc. She's due at Ellis next week. She's been waiting for this procedure for months.

I knew Gene was going to die, running machine or no running machine. I just didn't expect it to be so soon. Take care, Chris

## Gene

FROM: Pamela Robinson
TO: Chris Woods

What shocking news! How is Patricia coping? How are *you* coping—this death following hard on the heels of the loss of Kathleen? For so long we go on believing we're immortal, don't we? My boys still think death only happens to other people.

Poor Gene—poor Patricia. And poor you.

Sending love,

Pamela

X

## Re: Gene

FROM: Chris Woods
TO: Pamela Robinson

Hi Pamela, quit the poor everyone stuff. Gene's time was up. It's a better way to go than some of the alternatives. The folk at the dementia facility where I visit Mom's best friend have lost their marbles. Their bodies have stuck around too long.

Patricia does nothing but weep. 'How could he?' she says at regular intervals through her sobs. Like he did it on purpose. Like Gene dying is a personal insult to *her*. In between the wailing about him dying, she's wailing about him being her sweetheart.

'Wasn't he a good man, Chris?' she asks. 'In spite of everything?'

'In spite of everything,' I say, not looking her in the eye. 'Do you want me to make *pastitsio* with meat or with eggplant? I forget if you're eating meat again.'

'I'm eating meat,' she says, beginning to cry again. 'Gene loved your *pastitsio*. How could a fit, healthy man die?'

Then Karl, the son, comes around. He's really cut up. Patricia's cut up too. I don't want to make it sound like she's not.

So, in between listening to Patricia eulogising Gene, I'm listening to Mom complain about her neighbours. Her apartment is independent living, run by the Greek Orthodox church she's attended the last three thousand years. I don't know how long Mom can go on living there. She's eighty-seven, falling over every other day. She's trying to avoid going into a locked, high-care facility like her best friend, Eleni.

Mom's fought with everyone. She's got no friends left, so what's the point of staying? She's not talking to Angeliki

Pontisakis next door. Or Mrs Sarris on the other side, because Mrs Sarris knocks on the wall with her cane when my mother turns her television up too loud. Angeliki Pontisakis never got married. She's got no family and only my mother to pity her. Angeliki's sick and tired of my mother pitying her for never marrying and not having children. Last week Mom advised Angeliki she was cooking whatever she was cooking the wrong way. That's it, her last friend, gone.

Mom fought with her best friend Eleni, too, before Eleni lost her marbles. Most likely Mom doesn't want to visit Eleni anymore because she can't fight with her. My mother loves fighting, in case you were wondering. Take care, Chris

## Alive in the dark

FROM: Pamela Robinson
TO: Chris Woods

Hi Chris,

You're doing so much for everyone else—how does Mike cope while you're living at Patricia's? Doesn't he mind?

My news is that Claude has flunked maths—despite the tutoring—and the school's now trying, ever so subtly (for the moment, at least) to kick him out. I'm awake most nights—like tonight—worrying about him—as well as worrying about Raf, whose exams went badly too. He's in his second last year of school for God's sake, he doesn't have time to waste. The school's been in touch about 'unexplained absences' from both of them—some mornings I have to leave for work before they've left for school, then invariably I get a text from the school saying they've been marked absent. It's not as if I haven't made sure Raf and Claude set their alarms the night before—and I start ringing them the minute I get to work to make sure they're up. Now the school guidance officer wants to see me about Raf's name being mentioned in a text message of a student suspended for drug use.

If I'm not lying here worrying about Raf and Claude, I'm worrying about Baps, who's started wetting the bed. He's curled beside me now, a warm animal, back in my bed despite my best intentions, and I'm on constant alert for any sudden hot spill beneath me. It's 3 am here—I'm writing this on my phone.

Besides worrying about Claude dropping out, I worry about him running away—or else I worry about Raf running away. I worry about them falling through that safety net of houses and mothers cooking and cleaning and screaming at them—and ending up like my brother, dead of a heroin overdose at twenty-seven. Oh, Chris, if only you could have known my brother—he was the most soft-souled man, defenceless as a creature ripped from its habitat. Raf looks so much like him—as a kid Scotty had such a tender, open face, like Raf—a scattering of freckles across the nose, a signature tuft of white hair sticking straight up from the widow's peak at his forehead. Scotty was forever bringing home strays—small animals, or else the kids all the other kids wouldn't play with. Once, when we were children, we watched *Animal Farm* together—a cartoon version of Orwell's book—and Scotty was inconsolable when the old workhorse was taken off to the knackers. 'He's going to get melted to make glue?' he asked our mother. 'They put him in water and boil him?' He was crying so hard Mum had to take him outside into the cool and make him drink a glass of water.

For months afterwards, he woke screaming in the night—I was maybe nine or ten, he was maybe six, seven. I snuck him into my bed where he curled beside me—like Baps!—and I can still recall the feel of his breath on my skin, lightly fluttering. He had the boneless, soft flesh of a baby—I pretended he *was* my baby.

How did the hours carry Scotty curled safe in a childhood bed to a dismal room, a needle in his arm? How did he arrive at his final puny moment? And how can I defend my boys—or prevent them—falling into the same gaping maw? There's evil afoot—people taunting other people about lost cats, men dropping dead in streets. When I'm lying in the dark everything rushes in—every fear, every sorrow—the terrible emotional harm I've wreaked upon my sons—different in its particulars from the damage wreaked upon my brother, but surely as grievous.

How did Scotty come to lose his way? Is the same thing already happening—slowly—imperceptibly—to Raf? Claude? To Baps? I keep seeing Scotty's face in the funeral home and I'm back again in that fractured moment—the unearthly howl escaping my mother's lips. From my bed I see a spill of stars through the window—maybe the sun is out in Schenectady or perhaps it's obscured by clouds. Gene is dead—a man I never knew— also, a woman named Kathleen. My brother died—a long time ago—and here I am, alive in the dark, writing to an invisible woman I've never laid eyes on.

With much love,
Pamela

## Re: Alive in the dark

FROM: Chris Woods
TO: Pamela Robinson

Hey Pamela, listen, I'm sorry about your brother. But he was a different person with a different story to Raphael, Claude and Baptiste.

I work with students. I know about catastrophic thinking. For Pete's sake, you work in a library. Go look up some books on good sleeping habits.

Me, I'm so damn tired I fall asleep as soon as I hit the pillow. Yesterday I catered for Gene's wake, eighty-two people. Now Patricia's at Ellis and I'm staying at her place clearing out Gene's clothes before she gets back. After work Thursdays I head over to the twins' new rental for their English lessons.

I don't know if it's Muaz and Zahiya, or all Syrians, but they speak like poets. They tell me they want to speak like Americans. I guess they want to speak slang, though why the hell I wouldn't know. I could sit and listen to them speak their poetry all day.

Apart from teaching them slang, I'm teaching the girls to ride a bike. Yeah, I know. Someone gave them a bike and they want me to come over under the cover of darkness, so no-one will see them learning to ride. Their mom won't let a male near them.

'You don't want anyone to see you fall off?' I say. They think it's the funniest thing they ever heard. These gals are great gigglers.

'No,' says Zahiya. 'Our mother doesn't want us to ride a bicycle during the day.'

'Then why bother learning?'

'Because I always wanted to ride a bicycle,' says Zahiya.

'Americans say "bike",' I say.

So, the girls are going to ride a bike they can only ride at night, like in a dream.

It's got a light, I checked. Mike helped me buy bike helmets. Take care, Chris

## On washing-up meditation

FROM: Pamela Robinson
TO: Chris Woods

Hi again,

You're still at Patricia's? Why don't you sleep at your own house—isn't it only a few houses away?

Tonight we had some happiness. I've just finished washing up after a small birthday celebration for Claude—now Raf and Claude are only a year apart—one sixteen, the other fifteen—which sounds ridiculous. When they were small, they were often taken for twins—except they were like photo negatives of each other—Raf curly-haired and blond like his dad, Claude dark like me. But twins romantically suggests mutuality, accord, doubleness-as-one, while the relationship between Raf and Claude resembles that of Cain and Abel.

Deb was here—and Prisha—because civility in our house is most often achieved when other people besides ourselves are in attendance. Why can Raf speak to Prisha as if he is an ordinary human person with a tongue forming sounds against the teeth, but with me turn into a tortured prisoner, his tongue cut out? I hear all the news when other people are present—Raf has his eye on an impossibly beautiful girl from one of the private girls' schools, and Claude was telling Prisha about parkour—at which my ears pricked up. Is Claude going to be the next of my sons sneaking out at night, leaping between buildings in a single bound? I'm taking him and six friends paint-balling on Saturday for his birthday—it's the first I've heard about parkour. Like a trained sniper I immediately insinuated myself into position.

'It's beautiful to watch,' I said, intruding into their conversation, when in truth all I think about when I see young men and women hurdling buildings are cracked heads.

Prisha said she understands parkour to be as fierce a discipline as yoga.

Claude laughed. A laugh in our house is a flare in the dark, a promise that somewhere in the vast, unrecognisable universe there is a new day in front of us.

Washing up took a long time—but washing up to me is a meditation, like yoga, like parkour. I feel my hands working, fruitful, achieving something practical and good. I have a dishwasher but I prefer the cup, the soap, the rinsing. After I have righted my kitchen, I have righted the world for a moment.

Afterwards, I opened the doors to my sons asleep and faultless in their beds like children in a fairytale. I took out Claude's laugh again, unwrapped it, a song released to the room. I thought of him freeing it at the kitchen table, with Prisha—you should see Prisha's hair, gleaming, black, shining like oil streaming down her back—she is a good Indian daughter who reveres her parents as if they were already dead and in a framed photograph on the wall.

Signing off now so I can scoop my warm live child from his bed and hold the full weight of him in my arms as if he were nothing heavier than love. I'm going to try falling asleep while dreaming of you giving bike-riding lessons.

Pamela

X

## Bike-riding lessons

FROM: Chris Woods
TO: Pamela Robinson

Hi Pamela, most nights I'm not giving bike lessons. I'm sitting with Patricia at Ellis. Eva's up from the city, and she sits with Patricia nights I'm not there. 'You need sleeping pills,' I tell Patricia. 'Balls,' says Eva. 'She can't medicate her way through pain.' How does being crazy with grief help anyone? How is it good for a person not to sleep?

On the nights it's not my turn to sit with Patricia, I give my famous bike lessons. The girls' mom, Rima, makes me tea, special Syrian black tea, which tastes like boiled grass. I don't want to be rude, so I drink it, with as many spoons of sugar as I can. Rima doesn't speak English. We smile at each other, nodding our heads. She's fully veiled when she goes outside (head-to-toe black, even on these warm days, slat things covering her eyes). Inside, because I'm a woman in her private space, she shows me her face.

The streets are empty, save for a few folk sitting on steps out front taking the cool night air. The block where they live is long and straight, we can see cars coming miles away. The girls weave and sway, mostly keeping their long legs off the pedals. They want to ride with their legs straight out either side, toes pointed down, anticipating a fall.

'Use the pedals,' I shout.

One giggles while the other one rides, then they swap.

As you would expect, Muaz is the more fearless. In my head, I call her the evil twin. When she puts her feet on the pedals she falls off. She dusts herself down, gets back on again. The bike teeters and veers, Muaz struggling to stay upright, wobbling up the road. The streetlights are on her, she's suddenly away, her hair flying.

She reminds me of myself. I have never forgotten my youthful summer days in Greece, lying on beaches in my bikini, soaring down unpaved roads on the back of a motorbike. I was eighteen and summer felt like it would never be over. Take care, Chris

## Unanchored in Ashfield

FROM: Pamela Robinson
TO: Chris Woods

Hi Chris,

I think that's the first time I've heard one of your good memories—more, please. I like to picture you released, and not doing anything for anyone else. I like picturing you screaming down roads on the back of a motorbike. Here, it's Sunday night homework trauma aftermath time—I'm on the couch, three-quarters deep in a bottle of red wine. When you've finished bike-riding lessons and sitting up at the hospital with Patricia, can you do something for me by hopping on a plane to Sydney, Australia, to personally remove every electronic device from my sons' clenched fists? Can I join the Chris queue?

I've tried everything—reasoning, threats and withdrawal of privileges—but nothing works. I'm exhausted. They need laptops for their homework—unbelievably, they're provided by the school—and of course I supervise them while they're doing it. It's the wresting of the laptops away from them *after* they've done their homework that's the problem. Raf regularly ransacks my room now looking for the modem. My sons appear to believe that parental authority resides in physical intimidation or in inherent masculine force.

I've lost the fight—in some decisive way I can no longer recall I relinquished my parental power. I wanted so badly not to be my parents. I never wanted to be like my seething father, whose opinion was the only right one, who sent us to our rooms if we voiced a different view and criticised us for not being exactly like him. I never wanted to be the parent holding

111

my son in a headlock, like my father held Scotty, wrestling him to the ground with a pair of scissors, savagely lopping off his beautiful black hair. Scotty had dyed his white surfer's hair—usually stiff with salt—because he was at the peak of his Ramones devotion—refusing to go to my father's barber to get the same short-back-and-sides as our father. I never wanted a child of mine to act out of self-preservation—I wished to reason with my sons rather than bully them or frighten them or control them—but in my attempt to become a parent unlike my parents, I became no kind of parent at all. It's painful to see my impotence so openly exposed. I'm an ineffectual parent—and deeply ashamed.

Chris was the authority figure in our house—he was strict, *really* strict—and he didn't mind giving the boys a good whack when he thought they were out of line. We fought constantly over our opposing views on discipline—yet instinct somehow led me straight from my father—who didn't mind giving me and Scotty a good whack—to my husband. Isn't it a sort of miracle that a girl who spent her life running away from her father found her way to a disguised version of the same man? Or at least to a man she could miraculously turn into her father? I abdicated my authority—without Chris's ruling powers I'm flailing. The king is dead, the tyrant sacked—who is going to listen to a paper tiger squeak?

Chris's moods ruled our house in the same way my father's moods ruled my childhood. I knew the moment Chris walked in the door what the tone of our evening would be. He was often unhappy and frequently bad-tempered—he felt trapped by us. He doesn't like noise—and being noisy is a kid's job description. Chris found life impossibly hard when the kids were small—remember how close Raf and Claude are in age—and small children are wall-to-wall chaos: they spill things, they wake you up, they cry, they disrupt *everything*.

The first time we broke up Raf and Claude were under three. It happened because we were sitting at the kitchen table—both kids still in highchairs—when one of them, I can't remember which—threw his juice cup against the wall. We'd just had the wall repainted—and Chris shouted, 'Christ!', then immediately poured the contents of his wineglass over his own head before smashing it to smithereens on the table. I jumped up and shouted, 'For God's sake! You're the adult!' Chris leaped from his chair and hurtled towards me with what I can only call murderous intent. I ran towards the bathroom, glass splinters in my feet, and tried to push the door closed, but he was behind me, stronger than me, pushing it in. He grabbed me—pinned me against the bathroom wall—knocking my head hard against the tiles. 'If you want to run away, run!' I shouted. 'Have the courage to leave!' He shook me, hard, rattling my teeth, banging my head. I could see he hated me—I hated him too. But he let my arms go—shocked—and turned away. I rushed past him, past the children, down the corridor, out the door. I ran out of the house before I knew it—leaving my children behind. I was in fear of my life—or I thought that I was—but *I left my children*.

I didn't know where I was running to—I only knew I didn't want him to catch me. I crouched behind a car just as Chris spilled from the house—Claude on one hip—looking wildly left and right to see which way I'd gone. He went one way, then turned and came back in the direction where I was crouched. I moved to the other side of the car as he passed. My Claude—my darling son—in his arms. Me, my feet bleeding, a lump the size of an egg on the back of my skull—hiding—cowering—behind a car. Eventually he went back inside.

I didn't have any money on me so I walked all the way to a friend's house—a woman I didn't know very well. (This was London, far from my friends in Australia.) Sarah lived in New Cross, which was miles away. I can still recall that surreal walk—the feel of my dirty feet on the pavements, the sensation of being unhoused from my own body. I knocked on Sarah's door and she immediately went into domestic violence mode: *if he hits you once, he'll hit you again.* 'But he didn't hit me,' I said.

Chris moved out into his own flat for six months. He was really shocked—*he loved us.* I knew he loved us. At the same time, I knew he felt trapped by us—but loving us won. He was so contrite. We went to marriage counselling, me breastfeeding Claude, not yet a year old. Our lives falling around our heads, our shocked hearts full of love and anguish. Neither of us wanted our marriage to end—I didn't want the boys growing up without their father—and our anger fell away, just like that.

I don't want to give you the impression that it was only Chris who felt trapped and angry. I was often worn down by the days—which felt like the same endless day, over and over. Every inch of my life given over to the children—but I won't go there. Enough to say I was often as angry and miserable as him. You think I don't know it takes two to make a marriage fail? That my own failings weren't equal to his? I know I'm difficult to live with! I'm volatile, overly anxious, insensitive, and I live too much in my own head. Why do you think it took me so long to leave Chris? Because I know my own faults too well—and because I hold dear that old dream of a lifelong love. Chris never laid a finger on me again—*ever.*

Anyway, no Chris, no authority. It's the biggest surprise of my life, finding myself divorced and the boys separated from their father—it all happened so brutally. Right from the start, Chris refused to talk to me—we had maybe three or four telephone conversations before we left for Australia. He issued me with divorce papers before I even left France. Throughout, he continued to see the boys, to talk to them—his love for them never wavered—but his love for me quickly soured.

Now, here we are, unanchored—the father of my sons ten thousand miles away. I haven't told you, but I've been emailing Chris again—telling him about Raf's woes, the problems with Claude at school, Baps wetting the bed. Why won't he answer me? How can I keep believing I exist, if he keeps pretending I don't? But I'm comforted by the fact that he speaks to the boys. Sometimes I stand outside their bedroom door while Raf's speaking to Chris on the phone—all I can hear is Raf's monosyllabic replies. I never heard Chris speak so long in my life.

Tell me more of your happy memories—about eighteen-year-old Chrisanthi Xenia in her bikini under a Greek sun. Tell me about your hair flying.

With love,

Pamela

X

## Dialogue on Adulthood

FROM: Chris Woods
TO: Pamela Robinson

Dear Plato,

1. What's to tell? I was young. I didn't know about mort-gages or city taxes or about caring for anyone other than myself. Adulthood is not made of endless moments rushing down roads on motorbikes, your hair flying.

2. You think you can lie in a bikini in the sun all your life? The day comes when you must rise. You take your place as a citizen among the common crowd in the dark fields of the republic.

3. Sounds like your ex-husband got squeezed in the vice of life. *In extremis* everyone gets to the bottom of themselves. I guess your ex was trying to tell you a truth about himself. Truth gets delivered any way it can. The hard part is judging if a person *in extremis* reveals his worst self or his true self.

4. Walk away from the bedroom door. Walk away from the emails to your ex. Remember silence is sometimes a form of speech.

Take care, Socrates

## A man with teeth!

FROM: Pamela Robinson
TO: Chris Woods

Dear Socrates,

Thanks for the lessons in Platonic silence. Guess what? A MAN WITH HIS OWN TEETH HAS ASKED ME OUT. At least I think they're his own teeth—I haven't pulled them to find out. I see this bloke all the time—he's often sitting on the bench where I eat my lunch. Even though it's chilly I make a point of leaving the library, and I head up the road to this historic house in a park, so I can turn my face to the sun and recall the scope of human existence and my small blip within it. So one day I was sitting there, wrapped up in my coat on a cold bench, trying to imagine the passing movements of the world, when this man walked up and sat beside me.

I don't like strangers. I especially don't like strange men. I am already occupied, filled with irreconcilable grief for the husband I left—every man alive is simply a man who is not Chris. I'm as nuts as your neighbour Patricia.

'You work around here?' he asked.

'Obviously,' I replied and then immediately worried I sounded rude. 'I mean, yes. In the library. You?'

'Delivery driver. Office is over there.' He nodded vaguely in the direction of *over there* and I took the opportunity to covertly inspect him.

'I love this place,' he said.

I nodded politely.

'I love thinking about what it must have been like when a family still lived in it,' he said.

117

I remarked that ten families could live in it now. The house *is* beautiful—it must have been the house of the area in the nineteenth century—a Henry James-type house—all bannisters and pressed-metal ceilings and artfully proportioned windows.

'All those living people,' I said. 'Vanished. Dead.'

He laughed. 'Miss Cheery.'

I turned to look at him properly. He was older than me—maybe ten years older—silver hair in a buzz cut, eyebrows still black, a handsome face. He had that sort of generic Mediterranean face—do you know what I mean?—a beaked Roman nose, brown eyes, thin lips.

'I bet you like cemeteries,' he said, smiling.

I smiled back. 'How did you know?'

He tapped the side of his head. 'Me too,' he said. Then he stood up. 'Got to go. See you tomorrow?'

I nodded. I didn't mean to nod. I should have said, *Please, any interest in me is misguided. I am an inconsolable woman of contradictory emotions. I cannot live with my husband and I cannot live without him.* But I didn't speak—of course!—just continued smiling politely in that idiotic coquettish feminine way, all the while nodding my head.

I didn't go to the park the next day—or the next, or the one after that. When I judged that enough days had passed, I went back. He wasn't there—*phew*—I like to eat my lunch in peace, hoping the day will come when I will suddenly realise at the end of it that I haven't thought about Chris once. I was eating my lunch, thinking my thoughts, watching the sky and—*pouf*—he was suddenly there.

'G'day,' he said, sticking out his hand. 'I forgot to introduce myself. Nick Waterman.' To cut a long story short, Socrates—I'M GOING ON A DATE. I'm going because it's an alternative to falling into another bottle of wine or retreating to bed to let the days fall like petals until they cover my head and our troubles vanish. Next Saturday I'm 'walking out' with a white van delivery driver to Camperdown Cemetery. What could possibly go wrong?

Love,

Plato

## Re: A man with teeth!

FROM: Chris Woods
TO: Pamela Robinson

Hi Pamela, I thought you were like that other Pamela, guarding her virtue. Didn't you say you weren't making out with boys again? Go for it, honey, so long as you remember that three bowls of ice cream, a bottle of wine and a fresh, unopened lover don't assuage any grief for long.

Shopping doesn't alleviate pain either. Try telling that to my mom, who wants me to take her to the mall to inspect carpets. She plans on recarpeting her apartment. She's eighty-seven years old. I can't say: *Mom, why do you need a new carpet? The old one will outlast you.* So I say: 'Hmm.'

My mother says: 'I know what that "Hmm" means, Chrisanthi Xenia. Don't "Hmm" me.'

I say nothing.

'It's moth-eaten,' she says. 'Look over there. A hole as big as China.'

'Don't exaggerate, Mom. The carpet's fine.'

'Fine? So, it's fine for your mother to have a carpet with a hole as big as China? You'd have this carpet in your home?'

I look at the carpet. If I say yes, I'm in trouble. If I say no, I'm in trouble. I can't say 'Hmm' again.

'I don't know, Mom. It looks fine to me.'

My mother starts shouting that she can never have a straight conversation with me. She says I'm so good at complicating even the simplest things I could drown myself in a spoonful of water (except she says it in Greek which doesn't sound so polite).

'OK, Mom, if you want to look at carpets, we'll look at carpets.' Like I want to spend my day off looking at carpets. It's what my mother wants: as many people as possible spending their valuable free time on her. She feels validated if someone is taking her to look at carpets.

When I get home from looking at carpets I ring my sister.

'Yeah, she's a nightmare,' says Dora.

'Why is she *my* nightmare?' I say.

Dora lives in the city. My sister does not have a conscience, she has a neurosurgeon husband, a partnership in a big New York law firm, two high-achieving sons at Yale, a summer house on Martha's Vineyard and a three-million-dollar duplex on the Upper East Side.

'Oh, Chrissy, mom *loves* you!'

I try to let silence speak for me.

'Chrissy?' No-one but Dora calls me Chrissy.

'But how can you tell?' I say finally.

She laughs, as if I've cracked a joke. 'Of course she loves you! She's always telling everyone about you.'

Now it's my turn to laugh. 'Dora, you're the brag card for our mother. "Did I tell you my other daughter is a partner in one of New York's biggest law firms?"'

'Yeah, it's sweet,' she says.

Saturday I'm taking mom to inspect more carpets. Non-stop excitement here in Schenectady. Take care, Chris

## Sex and death

FROM: Pamela Robinson
TO: Chris Woods

Hi Chris,

Non-stop excitement here too—while you've been out with your mother looking at carpets, I've been walking in cold cemeteries with my suitor. I'd forgotten Richardson's *Pamela*—thank you for the reminder—and will henceforth resolve to lose my life sooner than my virtue. No chance of losing my virtue anyway—the entire time I was at the cemetery—trying not to step on graves, reading headstones, accompanied by this stranger who is not Chris—I'm thinking, *What do I care about a man I don't know called Nick Waterman? Why aren't I home with my children?*

It felt so strange, waiting to meet him at the gate. Was I supposed to kiss his cheek? Shake his hand? He solved the problem by leaning over and giving me a quick hug as we said hello—I felt as gormless as a fifteen-year-old. He led the way, marching off at a brisk pace, so that we were soon awash in headstones belonging to long-ago children who 'fell asleep,' their grief-struck parents combing the Bible—and no doubt the cold universe—for words of solace. I saw one psalm quoted twice—I copied it down on my phone: *And now, Lord, what is my hope? Truly my hope is even in Thee—Psalm XXXIX,* 7—both graves accompanied by a small stone angel, a symbol of Christian hope in this comfortless world.

Nick Waterman isn't a Christian—he's Jewish. I assumed he was Italian because of his Mediterranean face (not that you can't be both Jewish and Italian, of course). He's English—a bright boy from suburban Sutton who got an academic bursary to City of London School, a posh private boys' school near St Paul's.

'How did you end up in Sydney?' I asked, but what I was really asking was, *How did a City of London Old Boy end up as a white van delivery driver? Why aren't you a Tory politician or a banker?*

'Dope, basically,' he said.

'Huh?'

He smiled. 'The hippie trail. Magic Bus, a cave in Crete, Kathmandu, Cedar Bay . . . lots of spliffs.' He trailed off.

'Well, I hope you saw the face of God,' I said—possibly a little too harshly. Scotty started smoking dope at thirteen, and by twenty he'd tried every drug known to man. Of course I know dope is not a gateway drug for everyone, but because of what happened to my brother I've despised marijuana ever since.

'Weren't you a hippie once?'

God help me if he offered me a joint.

'I'm too young,' I said. All at once I felt too old, too tired, for this whole charade. The air was freezing.

'Listen to this,' he said, stopping at a grave, the ancient stone covering it broken in two. '*This grave is now my home / But soon I hope to rise / Mortals behold my tomb / Keep death before your eyes.*'

As if by magic, an extraordinary woman appeared—an old woman, seventy-five, eighty—a woman 'gussied up', as my mother used to say. She was wearing skin-tight black leather trousers, towering black heels, a black fishnet top with a black push-up bra sewn in, so that the old girls were out, waving through the net saying hello. Her hair was dyed blonde and her lips painted red and she wore blue eyeshadow—bright blue. Her eyebrows were drawn in with thick, dark pencil, which also rimmed her eyes. If she were twenty, you would say she was out to attract attention—and she would get it—the show-stopping, girl-stops-traffic kind of attention.

But she was old—*old*—and my instinct was to rush over and cover her up—and not because of the cold. She was a parody of an old tart—a man's worst nightmare. You know, the one where he goes to bed with a young beauty and wakes to find himself kissing a toothless old hag. She represented sex—her bosoms hitched up, her mouth red and puffed, offered up for mating like a baboon's bum. I found her repulsive—offensive to her sex, to me, to all women. I wanted her to salvage her own dignity—and mine.

She vanished among the headstones.

'Do you reckon she's a goth?' Nick said. He started to laugh.

'Don't laugh at her,' I said. 'If she was twenty-five your tongue would be hanging out. What is about old women and sex that scares you blokes?' The truth was I found her as frightening as he did—I just couldn't admit it.

'Old women remind men of death,' he said. He bent down, picked a wild poppy, and handed it to me.

It started to rain—not hard—but hard enough. 'We'd better go,' I said, feeling unaccountably cross.

'Do you want to come next Saturday? We haven't seen the most interesting graves yet.'

Over his shoulder I could no longer see the church, just the ruined graves and shrouded gloom of overhanging trees. It struck me that I was alone with a stranger in a cold, deserted graveyard.

'Sex and death, eh?' he said.

'Sex and death,' I repeated.

'What else is there?' he said, smiling.

With love from your sex and death correspondent,

Pamela

X

## Re: Sex and death

FROM: Chris Woods
TO: Pamela Robinson

Hi Pamela, mainly death and no sex around these parts. Mrs Sarris in the apartment next to Mom died. Mom tells me I've got the evil eye. Yeah, right, Mrs Sarris was two hundred years old and it's my fault she died. The only evil eye around here belongs to Mrs Calliope Pappas.

Mom's evil eye routine is a Chrisanthi Xenia special. Dora's immune to it. Me, I can tell the second Mom opens the door if she's pissed at me. I'm sixty-four years old today, still hoping to save my mother and make her happy. Happy birthday to me. Take care, Chris

### ♥♥☺Happy Birthday!!! ♪♥♥☺

FROM: Pamela Robinson
TO: Chris Woods

Sweetheart! I didn't know! I hope you had the most WONDERFUL day—despite Mrs Calliope Pappas and her evil eye. I hope Mike showered you with presents—and your rich sister too. ☺ Ask Dora to take you to a birthday lunch at MoMA so you can see the emojis hanging in the foyer—emojis which grew out of email exchanges exactly like ours—out of a human longing to connect, a longing which has existed as long as humans have, all the way back to hieroglyphics—because we can't help ourselves. Look at us, conveying human signs to each other across non-human virtual space—making faces from keyboard characters—using colons : and brackets ) to convey happiness, heartbreak—the living flesh behind the keyboard— emojis crossing time and space and human history, coming to you in Schenectady, New York, the United States of America from Sydney, New South Wales, Australia. And behind the symbol, a human creature of blood and breath—me—wishing you the happiest of birthdays ☺ ☺ ☺ ☺ ☺ ☺ ☺

With much love from your friend in virtual space,

Pamela :)

## Thanks

FROM: Chris Woods
TO: Pamela Robinson

Hi Pamela, thanks for the good wishes. Understatement is not your strong suit. I'm not really an emoji kind of person. ☺

Patricia's home, pissed at me for ditching Gene's clothes. I didn't ditch them, I gave them to charity.

'I know you're trying to help, Chris,' she says. 'It's not helping.'

This afternoon I went to the charity shop and got them back. Everything but the waistcoat she bought Gene for their first wedding anniversary. No, they didn't sell it. Probably Tina took it home. Tina who sorts the clothes. Tina who doesn't answer her phone.

Patricia is not happy when I get home sans waistcoat. 'Why would you do that, Chris? Throw away Gene's clothes without my permission?'

'Grief counselling,' I say. 'That's what grief counsellors say to do.'

Patricia tells me a thing or two about grief counselling. What Patricia doesn't know about grief counselling, marriage counselling or any other counselling is not worth knowing.

Apparently Gene's waistcoat is a signifier of love. It's not stitched with cotton, it's stitched supernaturally with every second, minute and hour of their happy lives together.

I think Patricia watched a different movie to me. Take care, Chris

## Divorce mourning wear

FROM: Pamela Robinson
TO: Chris Woods

Hi again,

You crack me up, Chris. I've got an idea for Patricia—remember how Greek widows used to wear black after their husbands died? We could bring that custom back especially for her—it seems as good a way as any of turning our mourning inside out. At the same time we could start divorce mourning wear—grey, say, or pale yellow—so everyone could recognise the other bereaved souls among us. Divorce parties are all very well—how could joy not visit a heart newly free of a bad marriage?—but if joy and grief are divorce's twin muses, then for every champagne cork popped in freedom's name, a flower is laid on love's grave.

Tell me—what is it about the hearts of men that the more you tell them, *Sorry, I'm not interested,* the more they want you? Nick seems like a perfectly nice man, but I'm not yet one year away from the worst days of my life—indeed, I feel myself to be still living the worst days of my life. How far from pain do you have to be before you can imagine life without it? It seems premature to be even considering another partner—preposterously inappropriate—shameless—like running off with your husband's best friend at your husband's funeral.

So why did I phone Prisha to tell her I'd be late, having agreed to have a drink with Nick after I found him loitering outside the library yesterday when I left work?

'How long do you think your sentence should be?' he asked when our drinks arrived.

'What sentence?'

'The sentence handed down by God when you left your marriage. The one that says you must live the rest of your life in penance for your crime,' he said. '*Salut.*'

We clinked glasses. 'Look, it's barely been a year,' I said.

'I know. I asked how long you think your sentence should be.'

I shrugged. 'Longer than a year.'

'Two? Five? What's appropriate?'

I shrugged again. 'I have three children I deprived of a father waiting for me at home. Maybe after they have left school—and home—I might consider another relationship.'

He laughed. He laughed!

'At this rate, you'll be eighty-five before you go on your next date. You know, these days kids don't leave home until their late twenties. Some don't leave till their thirties.'

'Well, I guess I'll wait,' I said primly. I felt like a character out of a Jane Austen novel who had wandered into the wrong century.

'Katie lived with me for six months last year,' he said. 'She's thirty-one.' Katie is the eldest of his three children—the younger two boys live in Melbourne—and she now lives in London. 'She was between jobs. Kids always see their parents as home base.'

I sat there, folding myself in.

'Listen, Pamela, I don't want to be your kids' new daddy. I just want to get into your pants.'

I looked at him, appalled.

He laughed again. 'You should see your face. I'm joking!'

I permitted myself a modest laugh.

He reached for my hand. 'I'm only half joking,' he said. 'You're gorgeous. You know that, don't you?'

And with that, this little piggy downed her drink and ran home.

Yours,

Pamela

## Re: Divorce mourning wear

FROM: Chris Woods
TO: Pamela Robinson

Hi Pamela, this Nick guy sounds like a fun distraction. From my end, the water you're swimming in is murky. Can you see your own feet?

Patricia's gone nuts over the missing waistcoat. Mike thinks I should replace it with a similar second-hand waistcoat. 'She won't be able to tell the difference,' he says. 'They got married last century. She wouldn't remember if it was black or tan.'

'You wouldn't remember if was black or tan, Mike. Patricia would know.'

Mike never notices the missing clothes I donate to charity. Not once has he asked, 'Where is my blue shirt with the brown trim?'

Mike's interest is in the walls, floors, ceilings and pipes of this old house. And in watching the same movie as me. Take care in the water, Chris

## Watching the same movie

FROM: Pamela Robinson
TO: Chris Woods

Hi Chris,
> The question is: do you like watching the same movie as Mike?
> Love,
> Your curious friend
> X

## Re: Watching the same movie

FROM: Chris Woods

TO: Pamela Robinson


Listen, Plato, Mike and I are the only two people in the world who know the same story. Take care, Socrates

## Tales to tell your mother

FROM: Pamela Robinson
TO: Chris Woods

Hi Socrates,

Scolding duly noted. I guess that's what the triumphant flag atop a fifty-five-year marriage represents. . . sharing the same story.

If you're right, I'm in the text message shallows and you're on the last pages of *War and Peace.* Nick's asked me around to his place for dinner and I'm devising tales to tell my kids about where I will be next Saturday night in the same way I devised tales to tell my mother when I was sneaking out to meet boys. How is it that my sons are the same age I was when I was sneaking out and now I'm the mother sneaking out telling the same old tales?

Deb's been for dinner—she's just left. We were talking about the Nick dilemma out in the sleep-out—Baps not asleep there in his own bed, of course, but in mine. Deb smokes, which is why we were in the sleep-out with the window open, even though it was freezing. Her advice re Nick is to open my arms wide. I told her I can't—I'm not ready—the children aren't ready—it's too soon—I feel sneaky, furtive.

'You're only going to his place for spaghetti, aren't you? You're not going to marry him,' she said, looking at me purposefully. I have a reputation for impulsiveness—I can't think why—me, who once decided to move to Fontainebleau because I liked the look of a certain peach tree against a certain stone wall.

'I don't know, it just feels wrong.'

'What's wrong is those kids walking all over you, Pam. They're exploiting your sense of guilt,' she said. 'Raf and Claude

134

aren't children, they're young adults. And Baps is not a baby. He should sleep in his own bed.'

'Oh, hurry up and finish your fag,' I said.

'Kids are remarkably resilient,' she said.

'Thank you, Ms Fraser. If I want truisms, I'll buy myself a Hallmark card.'

And then she told me—again—the story of her own parents' divorce, how her mother moving out was the best thing that ever happened. I remember Deb's mum, of course—she was the cool mum, the one with purple boots made for walking and the fake fur coat, who ran off with her much-younger boyfriend. Deb and her brother Paul were in high school and their parents bickered day and night. It was the first sound they heard every morning and the last sound they heard every night of their childhood.

'After Mum left I walked down the stairs and it was as if air had come back into the house,' she said. 'There was no screaming, no slammed doors, just the most beautiful silence.'

'Yeah, well, every divorce is different,' I said. 'Every unhappy marriage is unhappy in its own way. Chris and I didn't go in for door-slamming.'

I'd begged her to stay for dinner when she dropped in unexpectedly this afternoon—thus surreptitiously conscripting her for Sunday night homework trauma watch. 'You're not going home, are you?' I asked, panicked, when she rose to leave. Surely she wasn't going to leave me alone with my own children?

After we finished dinner the older two duly went without protest to the large desk I've set up in the sleep-out where they are supposed to do their homework in full public view—I can see their laptop screens easily from the doorway. I sneak up so fast they don't have time to close inappropriate tabs or shut down games.

Baps played games on Deb's phone until she told him he was frying his brain. *'Mais non!'* he protested when she took it away. Baps wants his own phone like his big brother's—he's been at me for months to buy him one. 'You're eight years old. You can have your own phone when you get to high school,' I said when he started to cry.

'Where's Souris?' Deb asked, trying to distract him.

Mercifully Deb stayed until Baps stopped crying, all homework was finished, every device turned off, and every boy tucked up in his bed—except for Baps, of course, who is asleep in mine.

What kind of incompetent moron needs the assistance of a grown-up to keep control over her own children? I'm scared to be alone with them.

Yours in shame,

Plato

X

## Re: Tales to tell your mother

FROM: Chris Woods
TO: Pamela Robinson

Hey Pamela, every incompetent moron's got more power than she knows. Your friend is right. Your kids are exploiting your guilt. Muscle up, Mom.

So, you're not the only one with an admirer. The evil twin's got herself a boyfriend. I'm the go-between for Muaz and her mom, between Muaz and her boyfriend. Like I speak Arabic. Like I speak the language of teenage love.

The problem is the boyfriend is not Syrian. He's a jock called Brandon. As far as I can tell he's a nice kid. Muaz asks me to supervise them on a trip to Central Park, where I get sunstroke while they ride bikes along the river, which is strewn with shopping carts.

It's Muaz who wants the chaperone, not Rima. She needs me, in case everything weird about Schenectady gathers itself in him. I guess she doesn't trust Brandon not to start breathing fire. The three of us go to the movies this afternoon, sitting in arctic AC watching a horror film. I'm the twenty-first-century version of that old Edwardian biddy chaperoning Lucy Honeychurch around Florence in *A Room with a View*.

In the restroom after the movie Muaz asks if she's permitted to kiss Brandon. How the hell do I know? Maybe in her culture she'll be engaged if she does. 'Do you want to kiss him, honey?'

Blood rushes to her face. She casts her eyes down. She nods. My, my. Am I supposed to give kissing lessons now?

137

'Mrs Woods, you are a very kind gal,' she says.

I pat her hand. I need to pick her up on her use of 'gal'. My heart pops like a cork when Muaz calls me a very kind gal. Take care, Chris

## A hard lesson

FROM: Pamela Robinson
TO: Chris Woods

Dear Chris,

What a pity you can't be a Kind Gal over here in Ashfield—I could do with some kindness. We've had another incident in the ongoing civil war that is our new family—I've just emailed the other Chris to tell him. I know everyone tells me not to bother, but how can I not when our sons are our mutual children, for whom we are jointly responsible? I'm not emailing him as a disguised plea for help (at least I don't think I am) or because I'm frightened of my own sons (although I am)—I'm appealing to his love for them, to his deep paternal instinct to protect them, irrespective of any issues he has with me. The only contact I have with him at the moment is the unfailing arrival in my Australian bank account of his monthly child support money. I want Chris to come to Australia to visit the boys. He might even consider staying, once he sees them—I don't know. I don't understand his absence in our lives. Maybe he's trying to teach me a hard lesson? But in what?

Last night's incident in the ongoing war was caused by a fight over Bap's new bed-wetting alarm. I know, I know! People a million miles away from family crisis find it astonishing that anything and everything can cause an outbreak in hostilities. Our doctor ran some tests and there's nothing physically wrong with Baps—no diabetes, no urinary tract infection—he's most probably just a very heavy sleeper. 'No bullying at school? Everything OK at home?' If I opened my mouth, my soul would fall out, so my mouth stayed shut. I didn't tell her Baps mostly sleeps with me.

There we were, me and Baps, discussing the business end of the alarm—the sensor that nestles in a slit cut into a sanitary pad and stuck in his underpants—when Claude came in.

'Baptiste's got his period! Baptiste's got his period!' he chanted. Baps looked confused—he doesn't know what a period is—but he instantly recognised a taunt when he heard one and he leaped at Claude with his small fists raised. I grabbed and held him, a red-faced bundle of fury, until he calmed down.

'Claude, that's enough!' I said. 'Go to your room.'

'I can't,' he said. 'Raf's banned me.'

'Oh, for God's sake.' I marched to the closed bedroom door, still carrying Baptiste. It was locked.

I'd hidden the key after too many fights about locking their shared bedroom door—but clearly I hadn't hidden it well enough.

'Open this door,' I said, as calmly and as authoritatively as I could.

Nothing.

'Raphael, open the door.'

Nothing.

I was still holding Baps, who was getting heavy.

'Come on, Raf, enough's enough,' I said. Even I could hear the desperation in my voice.

'Raphael?'

I put Baps down, but he stayed clinging to my leg.

'Open the door, love. I promise I won't get cross.'

'You're always cross,' said Claude, who was watching from the couch in the living room.

Silence from Raf.

I decided the best thing to do was nothing—I took Baps with me to the shared clothesline at the back of the flats where earlier I'd hung out yet another pair of sheets I'd washed after he peed the bed again. Back inside, I went about preparing dinner and asked Claude get started on any outstanding homework. I spent the entire evening with both ears cocked for the sound of a key turning in a lock.

Then I started getting angry—why should a sixteen-year-old boy have mastery over our household? I flew to the door and pounded on it. 'Open this door, Raphael.'

Silence.

'Now!' I thumped and thumped. I rattled the handle. I kicked the doorframe.

'Raphael!' I shouted.

I heard the roar of my own blood.

I heard the fury of my own impotence.

I kicked the door again.

'Raphael if you don't open this fucking door, I'll call the police.'

What idiot calls the police to open a locked door in her own house? I knew I shouldn't have said it as soon as the words left my mouth. I also knew I shouldn't make threats without going through with them. Was I really the fuckwit mother ringing the police because she couldn't get her son to open his bedroom door? How did I come to be living in this tinderbox, in a landscape so dry and imperilled as to ignite at the smallest spark?

He didn't open the door.

I called Deb, and she came around with her brother. They'd been out for dinner and were a little pissed. I haven't seen Paul in years. He's a barrister, a solid citizen, with a rock-solid marriage and four kids like ducks in a row—teacher, lawyer, architect, doctor—not a drug addict or dropout among them, or a flailing teenage son barricaded in a bedroom.

I don't think Paul could believe it. 'Come on, mate. Give your mum a break,' he said. I noted his use of 'mate'.

Raf opened the door.

'G'day, Raf. Paul Fraser, Deb's brother,' he said, sticking out his hand.

Raf shook it, acting for all the world as if he were merely joining the party rather than emerging from a six-hour stand-off.

We sat awkwardly together in the living room, me offering up unwanted food and drink.

'What are you planning on studying, Raf?' Paul asked. 'You're already a step ahead of the pack being bilingual.'

Raf kept his head down.

'He's always been good at art,' Deb said. 'I've got one of his paintings.'

Desultory conversation continued until Paul tried out his counselling skills.

'Our parents divorced when we your age,' he said.

Raf kept his eyes averted. I recalled being sixteen myself, words spoiling in my mouth. Baps was drowsing in my lap, half asleep—Claude had not long gone to bed.

'To be honest, it was a big relief,' Paul said.

Raf said nothing. 'Are you divorced, Maman?' Baps asked, sitting up.

I stroked his head. 'I told you before, darling,' I said.

He started to cry.

Not long after, the gathering broke up. Raf went to bed without protest and, once again, I neglected to speak a single word from the book of my heart.

I've just gone to check on him—his bed is empty. In the kitchen there's a spray of tomato sauce up the walls, as in a Jackson Pollock artwork. It's a message even I can decipher.

Love,

Pamela

X

## Handy Andy

FROM: Chris Woods

TO: Pamela Robinson

Hi Pamela, I guess you're going to greet your kid when he comes home with a cloth and a bottle of Handy Andy. Also, throw away the bedroom key and give him a kick in the butt from me. Raf should meet Muaz and Zahiya, who no longer have a father. Not even one living in Paris.

The girls were over Sunday to witness my annual swim in our pool. I told Mike to vamoose.

Rima took them shopping for new burkinis, the girls doing the translating. I'm expecting a Muslim version of a bikini. Turns out a burkini is a head-to-toe lycra bodysuit, complete with built-in hijab and ankle-length over-skirt. Brazilian-bikini-wax wear it is not. Me, I'm wearing my size 26 floral swimsuit with a voluminous skirt falling from the bosom.

'Laugh at your peril,' I say.

Zahiya looks confused. 'Never mind,' I say, patting her tan hand. These girls have lovely dark complexions. I'm whiter than a snow goose.

Zahiya and Muaz have been in nothing deeper than a bathtub. They've never seen the ocean. It took the best part of an hour to coax them to dip as much as a pinkie. When they finally get in, they squeal and giggle so hard I start to worry they'll drown.

'Concentrate, Muaz,' I say, which only makes her giggle harder.

She's swallowing so much water I tell her she's going to capsize.

'I am not a ship, Mrs Woods,' she says, going under again.

Swimming lessons are beyond me, so I try to teach them to float. I forgot how being in water makes you shed your body.

The evil twin is begging me to let her boyfriend come swimming next weekend. The girls finish school for the summer Friday. You should see those girls in the pool. Keep strong, Pamela. Take care, Chris

## A man in the picture

FROM: Pamela Robinson
TO: Chris Woods

How beautiful it sounds, the three of you weightless in the pool. When I was a child in a swimming pool I spent most of my time underwater, entranced by the muffled world, its transformed visions and noises—my mother frequently hauling me up by the strap of my swimming costume, believing me to be drowned. I loved it down there. Right now, if I can't fall into an enchanted sleep for a thousand years, my second choice would be to lie unreachable on the bottom of a swimming pool.

Awake and out of the water, I'm the one standing at the door with the Handy Andy. Can I get Raphael to clean the wall?

I cannot.

I've asked him politely.

I've commanded him.

I've shouted at him.

I've begged.

Meanwhile, the tomato sauce lies congealing on the walls. It'll need to be scraped off now—and probably by me. Prisha couldn't understand it when she dropped Baps off. 'Mrs Robinson, there is foodstuff here,' she said, pointing to the marks, as if I might not have seen them. 'I know, Prisha, thank you,' I said. 'I'm waiting for Raf to clean it off.' She looked confused. 'Have you not asked him?' I nodded. 'It's a long story, Prisha,' I said. Too long to unravel—too long for my mouth—too far off in the distance to see where the first word was misspoken and the story went wrong.

I'm just back from my spaghetti date with Nick. Deb granted me the night off—she said I should go out for a breather while she kept an eye on the boys.

And how entrancing a date I proved to be—banging on about being unable to control my kids makes such for such scintillating conversation, no? If Nick expected to get into my pants he was sorely disappointed. Perhaps I imagined talking about my inadequate parenting skills to be a diversionary tactic to avoid said pants. If so—success! I left my with my virtue unassailed.

We spent most of the evening discussing our children. 'Katie told me when she was thirteen I'd ruined her childhood because I wouldn't let her wear a dress which revealed her tits,' he said, as if this anecdote might be compared to my son barricaded in his bedroom for six hours while on a good behaviour bond.

Am I turning into one of those people who compare miseries on a scale of one to ten so that the death of a child rates a ten but the fallout from an acrimonious divorce a four or a five? When I was thirteen I told my father to fuck off—and he did, appalled—because I was cornered fully dressed in a shower recess after he had chased me through the house, failing to understand I did not find it amusing to be chased by a drunk trying to tickle me, even after I had already shouted at him to stop. Does that rate as a one or a two?

'Write out a behavioural contract, Pamela,' Nick said. 'Get Raphael to agree to a set of rules the family abides by. We had one when our kids were teenagers.' Besides Katie, he has two fully functioning adult sons.

I wanted to know about Nick's family life, his marriage, the exact details of his separation and divorce. According to Nick, he and his wife Claire grew tired of one another. No infidelity, no conflict, no acrimony—they simply got to the end of each other and recognised it was time to move on.

'You make it sound as if marriage has a shelf life,' I said.

He smiled. 'Some marriages do.'

He thought it might be a good idea for him to come over to the flat for dinner some time, meet the boys, so that they could see there was a man in the picture.

'Uh-uh,' I said. 'There's no way that's a good idea.'

'Why not?'

'Why throw another match into the flames?' I asked. I may be a parenting catastrophe, but I know a fire when I see one.

'Boys are pack animals,' he said. 'There needs to be a top dog.'

'I'm supposed to be top dog,' I said.

'How's that working out for you?'

How did a woman who believes herself to be a feminist end up with a husband who is top dog? How did I contort and abase myself to fit the traditional shape of a patriarchal marriage, producing a litter of male puppies whose ears are primed to obey only the snap of their male leader? I could blame my mother for her maternal blueprint—for falling into femininity's petticoats and swallowing every spoon-fed word of the story of girls whose lives begin only with the arrival of boys; for believing physical beauty to be a woman's greatest asset and for allowing my father to swell into his monstrous full-blown shape until he filled every corner of the house. I could let loose that old rage at her failure to demonstrate a single blazing sign of independent thought or life. If, for a long time, my most violent wish was to escape my father, it was also to avoid my mother's fate—to strike out on a different path and start a fire of my own. But who does that old rage help? Not me—and not her, who died with her *we were married for fifty-five years* flag

still flying—and certainly not Raphael, Claude and Baptiste.
I'm the one who made the path, who chose the top dog, who
doused the flames.

Yours,

Pamela

X

## Devil's dust

FROM: Chris Woods
TO: Pamela Robinson

Hey Plato, the question to ask isn't how it happened but what you're going to do about it. Self-flagellation isn't a recognised behaviour in the dog kingdom.

I don't know much about boys. I know about dogs. I can tell you about sisters. I can tell you Dora's my mother's favourite child, whose beautiful golden hair matched her golden heart. I can tell you I hated my sister so much I stabbed her in the leg with my mother's sewing scissors when I was twelve.

Muaz is top dog in her family. She and Zahiya hardly fight. If Muaz fights with her sister, it's because of her fiery heart and Zahiya stepping in to break up whatever mess Muaz has gotten herself into. Muaz shouts at Zahiya to butt out. Zahiya shouts back.

Muaz works herself up to a frenzy watching live blogs and YouTube clips of Syria. Endless shaky videos of their hometown, reduced to rubble. I try to imagine what it must be like for them watching their personal destruction not once, in real time, but twice, three times, over and over. When Mom and her sister and Yiayia left Greece for America after the war they may as well have left the planet.

Muaz finds a video containing a small shot of her best friend's house getting bombed, reduced to a cloud of dust.

'A bomb cloud is everything a house was,' says Muaz. 'Concrete, wood, flesh. It is the dust of the devil.'

I tell her to stop watching YouTube. It's not good for her, one half of her here in the USA, the other half in Syria.

'What do you know about it?' she says, her eyes flashing. 'What do you know of the dust of the devil?'

Zahiya tells her to shut up. I taught Zahiya the meaning of 'shut up'.

So, today Muaz tells me Syrian YouTube satellite images have gone fuzzy, a strange white cloud obscuring the picture, and they can no longer see anything. 'Assad has thrown a veil into space,' says Muaz, 'but free Syria is still alive in countless numbers of its daughters and sons.' I told you Syrians speak like poets. Take care, Socrates

## A bomb cloud

FROM: Pamela Robinson
TO: Chris Woods

Hi Chris,

How flimsy is our little bomb cloud of tears—the fallout from one inconsequential divorce among millions—next to that cloud of concrete, wood and flesh.

Love,
Pamela

## Re: A bomb cloud

FROM: Chris Woods
TO: Pamela Robinson

Hi Pamela, the only bomb cloud over Schenectady is Patricia fighting with her son Karl over Gene's estate. He left everything to Karl.

Do I think he did it out of spite? Yes.

Do I want to help Patricia fight the case, taking her to countless meetings with attorneys in my lunch hour because she needs what she calls 'moral support'? I do not.

So, who's the bozo riding shotgun with Patricia into meetings with guys in shiny suits?

That would be me, carrying papers, taking notes, listening hard with both my ears because Patricia is weeping so loud she can't hear. 'Why? Why?' she wails and I'm crooning, 'Shhh, shhh,' in my polite student counselling voice, when inside I'm screaming, 'SHUT THE CRAP UP!'

Every night, after I've been to another meeting in some attorney's office with Patricia, I'm on the phone to her for another hour. She wants to go over everything the guy said, because she was crying too hard to listen. Days when we haven't had a meeting, she still phones, wanting to talk about the treachery of her son or Gene's cruel behaviour. Patricia's forgotten how recently she extolled Gene's virtues.

This woman is a marriage counsellor. This woman has a degree or a diploma in—what? Active listening? Interpersonal skills? Being annoying? So, I'm on the couch, my feet up, my ankles blown up like balloons because of the heat, Kathleen's three-legged cat in my lap, Mindy trembling on the floor, listening to Patricia going on about Gene. She's still fighting a man dead in his grave. Maybe she'll keep fighting when she's dead too, her grave next to his, a little tunnel between the coffins so their bones can sneak across and rattle and clank and annoy the crap out of each other. Take care, Chris

## Martyrdom

FROM: Pamela Robinson
TO: Chris Woods

Hi again,

Oh, dear—sad, crazy Patricia. Though I fear I'm more like her than I care to admit—clinging to the wreckage. Can't you tell her you've got a life to live too?

This comes to you on the twelfth and final day of the Martyrdom of the Tomato Sauce—to let you know I cracked and cleaned it up. I suppose I could have kept it on the wall forever as a relic of my martyrdom, but on the advice of my chaste nominal new boyfriend as well as my old best friend, I chose the Handy Andy. 'Fight about them going to school instead,' said Deb. 'You're allowed to fight about that.'

'Listen, babe,' said Nick (he has started calling me 'babe'— SEND HELP). 'You can't die on a hill over tomato sauce. Save your fire.'

But every morning the stain on the wall was a reminder of my failure as a parent—and the same every evening when I got home. My thinking went like this: if I can't get my kid to clean a spray of tomato sauce off a wall, for fuck's sake, how can I get him to school on time, let alone safely to shore and a happy adult life? The congealing sauce was my battlefield—his will against mine, my authority against his. It was a war I needed to win.

Now it's over, and I'm waiting for Raf to get home. I'm going to try and not act like a vanquished army, yielding up my martyr's crown.

Yours in defeat,
Pamela

## Re: Martyrdom

FROM: Chris Woods
TO: Pamela Robinson

Hi Pamela, so, I guess you martyrs have cornered the market.
Patricia and I had a big fight. I dropped her home after another
meeting with her attorney. I tell her she should drop the case,
give everything to Karl like Gene wanted. 'Let it go, Patricia,'
I say. 'Walk away.'

'And where would that leave me? Homeless? At my age?'
This time she doesn't start crying, she starts shouting. 'What
would you know about it? Are you having to fight to stay in
your own home? Is your own husband so vengeful?'

First, I start placating her. I'm saying all the right things,
making all the right sounds. Then, all at once, this fury kicks
in. I'm thinking: why doesn't Patricia ever ask about my life?
What about *me*?

'Oh, shut the crap up,' I say. I sort of yell at her, to be honest.
Patricia looks like I've hit her in the face.

'Get out of my house,' she says.

So I go.

You know what? It felt good. I felt a fat, satisfied hatred.

What I said was not very Christian. I guess I'm a bitch like
my mother. Take care, Chris

## Eating the air

FROM: Pamela Robinson
TO: Chris Woods


My goodness, Socrates, you're going to start insisting on your
own air? Patricia sounds *so* bloody annoying, I feel like you've
smacked her one for the team—God, now *I* sound like a bitch.
But isn't it true that people like Patricia suck up all the oxygen?
 Love from your other friendly oxygen thief,
 Plato

## Re: Eating the air

FROM: Chris Woods
TO: Pamela Robinson

Hi Pamela, I think I already told you about Tracey, my colleague at SUNY. Work wouldn't give me her home address when she had another miscarriage and I wanted to visit. This time the doctors stitched her up so the foetus doesn't fall out. You'd think they'd call her condition something different to 'incompetent cervix,' as if her cervix failed math.

So, yesterday she loses the baby. Luckily I now have her cell number.

She picks up straight away.

'Do you want me to visit, honey?'

Silence.

'Tracey?'

More silence.

'Tell me what you need.'

I hear crying. I think: right, I'm going over. Through her sobs, she gives me her address. I tell Mike I'm going out. I pick out the best bunch of flowers I can find at Price Chopper on the way over.

Tracey's husband, Todd, opens the door.

'I'm so sorry,' I say, holding out the flowers.

He takes the flowers but doesn't invite me in. 'Thank you, Mrs Woods. It's kind of you to come all this way but Tracey doesn't want visitors right now.'

I must have looked surprised. 'She really appreciates your kindness,' he says, moving to close the door.

'She doesn't want company?'

He shakes his head. 'She's pretty bad,' he says, looking behind him.

'Can I help?'

He shakes his head again. 'Thank you, no,' he says, and repeats, 'I'm sorry you came all this way.'

Back in the car I glance up at the house. I see Tracey's face behind a curtain, gone in a flash. I feel her loss, radiating all the way down to me. Take care, Chris

## Re: Re: Eating the air

FROM: Pamela Robinson
TO: Chris Woods

Chris, tell me if I'm falling over friendship's boundaries—or fucking erasing them—and if my ongoing domestic dramas are too unbelievably stupid to stomach. I'm conscious we've come to grief before—but right now emails to you are the only way I'm able to gather my thoughts, which burst from me, flying everywhere. Writing everything down is the only way I can catch them.

Tonight violence smashed the house down. Claude 'stole' a T-shirt of Raf's then ran into my room to get away from his raging brother. Raf was pushing the door trying to get in while Claude pushed from the other side trying to keep him out, when—*crash*—the door fell in. Claude's hand went straight through the glass at the top of the doorframe.

Blood everywhere—spurting so hard I thought he'd cut an artery. 'Christ, Raphael! Now look what you've done!' It was out of my mouth before I knew it—and then there was blood and screaming and rushing around looking for something to wrap up Claude's hand. I took in Raf's white, stricken face—even his shaved head looked deathly pale—I saw his look of abject terror in the midst of pandemonium—and then I bundled Claude into the car and headed for emergency, though I found it hard to drive properly because I was terrified Claude was bleeding to death. The towel I'd wrapped his hand in was already soaked—I kept watching him to see if he was going to pass out. I was driving and watching Claude at the same time. *'Maman, conduis simplement!'* he shouted—just drive!—his head resting back on the seat, his eyes closed. Baps was in the back, bawling his head off.

At the hospital, they saw him straight away. Claude, now visibly trembling, his face stiff with fear and his hair black against his pale skin, offered a faint smile as he was whisked away. I was left with a still-howling Baps, my Medicare card, and a towel covered in blood—and then I remembered Raf at home.

'How long should I wait?' I asked the nurse. She turned up her hands.

I didn't know whether to go back to Raf or stay in case Claude needed me. I was standing in the middle of the emergency room, holding Baps, surrounded by drunks, crying babies and a moaning woman with a grotesquely swollen stomach which looked as if it were about to burst. It was like a Hieronymus Bosch scene and I was part of it—fully part of it—the hapless single mother who failed to set appropriate boundaries, whose brawling kids end up in emergency, overrun with feelings they can't properly, necessarily, contain.

After hours—*hours*—Claude was removed to a ward and an appointment was made with a hand surgeon. The nerves and tendons are severed in his little finger. He's booked in for surgery this morning. I kept expecting to be referred to Children's Services, but no-one seemed overly concerned with how it happened. No-one questioned me.

How violently must a young man feel to smash a door down? How furious the force of his distress? Of course I recognised Raf was enacting upon the physical world the brutality of his family's extinguishment—but I also knew I needed to get to him fast, so I dashed to the car, carrying a sleeping Baptiste, driving too fast—and found the flat empty. I picked up Baps again—still sleeping—and laid him on the back seat of the car. God forbid that he should wake up in the flat and find no-one there.

I drove around the streets for hours—down side alleys and along main roads, past the Fake Grass House—looking everywhere for a young man, his shaved head covered by a hood. Pain has split us open with its knife—Raf, Claude, Baptiste, Chris, me. I drove through artificially lit streets, no moon, only me and pain's blooded knife.

Finally, I stopped the car and walked, thinking I might see more that way. I left Baps, still asleep, safely locked inside, hoping to Christ he wouldn't wake up. There were so many streets, so much city! A boy could easily vanish. Raf's face kept morphing into Scotty's face at the funeral home—I felt the same sense of unreality and dread. I walked and walked, calling and calling and then, miraculously, there he was, illuminated by a streetlight, sitting cross-legged on the edge of the footpath.

Just in time I remembered not to run; he was like an animal easily startled. I walked towards him slowly, soundlessly, telling myself not to cry. As if he sensed my presence, he turned his head and watched my approach. When I reached him, I kneeled on the footpath and he fell into my arms. 'Shhh, shhh, it's OK,' I crooned. 'It's all right, Raphael.' And then he was sobbing—trying to tell me he was sorry—he was so sorry—*désolé, désolé*. We're on a dirty footpath, crying in each other's arms, except I was supposed to be the anchor, the mother—and anchors don't cry. I felt myself growing steely, my tears hardening, my arms holding firm. My child was in them—safe, held. We were in the dark, lit by unspeakable love. Oh, Chris, what have I done? I should never have left my children's father.

I'll understand completely if you want to stop our correspondence.

Love,

Pamela

## From Chris

FROM: Chris Woods
TO: Pamela Robinson

Honey, I'm not going to quit emailing. That gives you one less thing to worry about.

My advice is to get your friend Deb to move in. She can sleep in Baptiste's bed. He's sleeping in your bed anyway. If I could, I would move in myself.

Maybe Raf or Claude can stay with another family for a while, give everyone a breather.

You've dropped the anchor. What's the captain going to do now? Take care, Chris

## Re: From Chris

FROM: Pamela Robinson
TO: Chris Woods

Raf just hit me. I turned the modem off and ran out the door, the modem in my hand, him shouting, *Give me that back, you cunt.* He wrenched it from my hand, then punched me hard in the side of the head with the full force of his fist. I saw his face, transfigured by hate—I saw myself as he saw me, the goddess of destruction, the possessed woman wrecking everything for nothing but love of annihilation. There was a ringing in my ear—distorted sounds—the loud beat of my blood. I was both myself and also Raphael—I knew he wished to smash everything—me, him, the flat, the planet. It wasn't the modem he wanted—he wanted to spin the world, to tilt it on its axis, to turn everything back to what it was before. He was trying to reverse time.

## Some help

FROM: Chris Woods
TO: Pamela Robinson

Pamela, here are a couple of numbers I googled in Australia. The first is a crisis line called Lifeline. It's a 24/7 counselling service. The number is 13 11 14. It's toll-free. The other service I found is called Relationships Australia. It's got a program specifically for families going through separation and divorce. The website says it has family counselling and individual counselling. The number is 1300 364 277.

It's domestic violence, Pamela. Even if it's your son and not your partner. You know what to do. Your kids need help. *You* need help. God bless, Chris

**URGENT**

FROM: Chris Woods

TO: Pamela Robinson

Pamela, is everything all right? Did you call those numbers? I feel helpless, like I can't do anything from here. Please send the email address of your friend Deb. Take care, Chris

## Re: URGENT

FROM: Pamela Robinson
TO: Chris Woods

Hi Chris,

Everything's OK. I don't need you to email anyone. Deb's here and Raf's staying at a friend's house. I'll ring work in the morning and arrange to take a week off—maybe a fortnight. I've got an appointment with a family therapist a friend of Deb's recommended. THANK YOU.

With love,
Pamela
X

## Your phone number

FROM: Chris Woods
TO: Pamela Robinson

Hi Pamela, I'm glad Deb's there. What's your number? I want to call. Take care, Chris

WED 17/07 1.03AM

**Re: Your phone number**

FROM: Pamela Robinson

TO: Chris Woods

Hi Chris,

Honestly, I'm all right—you don't need the expense of ringing international mobile phone numbers. I'll give you my number, because you asked for it: +61 (0)435 832 3 ____ But *please*, don't call. I'll tell you when I'm up to speaking—I can't face talking to anyone right now.

It's eerily peaceful—the world silent after its terrible roaring. I'm off work for two weeks, Deb's staying and Claude's out of hospital and back at school, his hand bandaged. Raf is still at his friend's. I haven't spoken to him yet. The mother of his friend is a school guidance officer—what are the chances?—and she's already arranged for him to see a child psychologist. I've talked to her on the phone—her name's Marion—I'm going around to meet her today. She says it's fine for Raf to stay for as long as we need.

'My only proviso is that Raphael adopts Ben's study routine,' she said, 'since this last term is effectively an HSC prep term.' She went on about year eleven being a critical year for kids sitting the HSC next year (that's like your SATs, I guess)—AS IF I DIDN'T KNOW!! For Christ's sake, that's what this whole thing has been about—ostensibly at least: me trying to get Raf to stop playing computer games and start studying!! I have no idea what he's told Marion, but I immediately felt myself placed in the negligent mother box, as if I've been out on the town every night drinking cocktails with passing men instead of staying home trying to get Raf to study. I've only been out on a school night two or three times the whole time we've been in Australia! I haven't slept with anybody! My instinct was to defend myself, but I'm so wordless these days, so ashamed, not a squeak came out. How did a university-educated woman with a brain not addled by drugs or drink end up with a son who hits her?

Not only can I no longer speak, I can't hear properly—I can't think. My desperate, broken children—how frightened they must be.

Pamela

## Thank you

FROM: Pamela Robinson
TO: Chris Woods

Hi Chris,

Well, I don't know how I expected you to sound—but it wasn't like that. Thank you so much for your kindness—I'm deeply moved you took the trouble to call. I'm sorry I wasn't very communicative—I'm really tired and it's the middle of the night—but I *was* listening, I assure you, and I'm going to do everything you suggested, I promise. Now—*please*—stop trying to save Muaz and Zahiya and Tracey and Patricia and your mother and me and everyone else on the planet. Go spend some time on yourself.

Love, and thanks, from Pamela

X

## How are you doing?

FROM: Chris Woods
TO: Pamela Robinson

Hi Pamela, did you see the therapist today? You should have been seeing a family therapist long before this. We pretend this world is ruled by rational heads and civilised emotions. Truth is, our emotions live back in the Stone Age. They're always there, crying in the dark. For Pete's sake, not everything is your fault. Take care, Chris

## Re: How are you doing?

FROM: Pamela Robinson
TO: Chris Woods

Hi Chris,

Yes, I saw the therapist or the psychologist or whatever she's called. Actually, I do know—she's a proper psychiatrist with training in good, old-fashioned psychoanalysis. She specialises in adolescents and families, and the first thing she told me was I should not assume she could provide me with a quick fix. Her name's Tünde—she's Hungarian—and she seems reasonable enough. A bit chilly and remote for my tastes, but I'll cling to anyone or anything right now. Her office is like the living room of a house in a magazine—expensive rugs, original paintings and rare flowers in beautiful vases. There are inappropriate photographs of her family—presumably a family where no-one puts their hands through doors or hits mothers in the side of the head or dies of heroin overdoses. *Tell me how to fix it*, I was thinking. *Tell me how to raise the dead.* Instead, I was mute. I've lost my voice, my critical underpinnings—I don't know how to have proper thoughts.

We sat there—in silence mostly, except for my sobs—me thinking, *this is costing me a hundred and fifty fucking bucks.* I didn't know where to start. Whenever I started to talk, I started crying. I remembered something my mother once said: *Why do you remember only the bad things? Why do you only talk about your father in a negative way, forgetting all the good things he did for you?* I don't know is the answer. Something happened to me, to me and to Scotty. I remember the wrong things.

I remember creeping out of bed one night to find my mother crying in the kitchen. When I saw her I thought—with a great rush of hope—*At last the truth is spilling out!* But when I asked what was wrong she said nothing was wrong—and why would I think something was wrong when everything was absolutely fine? We were a happy family! I was the unhappy one who couldn't tell the difference between a truth and a lie, who couldn't laugh like other happy girls, shopping for clothes with their happy mothers, tripping light and laughing across the surface of that beautiful veneer everyone lived behind. I was the one who couldn't trust my own eyes, much less my own judgement.

Chris, I feel like an invalid—as if I'm the one with the smashed fingers—as if I'm recovering from some unknown illness. I'm undone.

Love,

Pamela

## Therapy

FROM: Chris Woods
TO: Pamela Robinson

Hi Pamela, it's good you saw the therapist. As long as your therapist is not called Patricia. Hang in there, honey. The anchor's down, the ship steadied. Somewhere within reach, there's land. Take care, Chris

TUE 23/07 4.55PM

## Truth

FROM: Pamela Robinson
TO: Chris Woods

Hi Chris,

I'm just back from the surgeon's follow-up appointment with Claude—my first foray as an ordinary mother into the outside world. I felt unskinned—as if everyone was looking at me; as if everyone knew I had a son who hit me. I was shaking so much I was scared the surgeon would notice, but straight away he launched into a report about how the operation went. He said he was confident Claude will regain full use of his hand, provided he keeps up his weekly physiotherapy appointments and daily exercises. I had no idea Claude's use of his hand was even at risk! I was so shocked when he said it. Claude, our sunniest child, our chatterbox we joked could talk underwater—he's going to need twelve weeks of physio—twelve weeks!—and he's got to do daily hand and finger exercises. So now I'm going to be on his case not only about doing his homework, but about doing his hand exercises as well.

There's only Claude and me in the flat at the moment—Prisha's taken Baps to the park and I asked Deb to nip out, because I was hoping to spend some time with Claude alone. He's been so quiet since he came home from hospital—he stayed two nights—I can barely get a yes or a no out of him. He still looks so pale, his eyes dark and luminous, evading mine. There we were, sitting at the kitchen table, speechless—Raf's usual chair opposite Claude's cavernously empty, the carrot cake Deb cooked catching in our throats. All the words I wanted to say had fled.

176

'Are you OK, sweetheart?' I finally asked into the silence.

'Yeah,' he said, not looking at me. He wears his hair long, so he can hide behind it; a sheet of dark hair fell across his face.

'You know both Dad and I love you,' I said.

He leaped from his chair. 'Why do you talk about Dad all the time? He never talks about you!' He rushed to his bedroom, slamming the newly fixed door.

I hardly mention Chris's name! The rare times I do it's to reassure the boys they're still loved—jointly. Maybe I shouldn't be talking for Chris anymore. Maybe to Claude I'm like my mother, sugar-coating the truth, when surely one single truth still stands among the ruins? The truth of love?

Pamela

## Re: Truth

FROM: Chris Woods
TO: Pamela Robinson

Hi Pamela, I guess I pissed Patricia even more than you annoy your sons. She's written a letter to Mike, my own husband, listing my sins. He should know exactly the kind of person he is married to. My sins are: being passive aggressive (naturally), getting over-involved in other people's lives so that I manipulate them into a position of dependence, and then using my power to cause maximum psychological devastation by withdrawing my emotional support.

She ends her letter in capitals: TELL CHRIS BEFORE SHE CAN HELP HEAL ANYONE ELSE, SHE HAS TO HEAL HERSELF.

Mike thinks I should ignore it. 'She's psycho. Forget it,' he says. What does he care? He's down in the basement building a new kitchen bench. His main worry is the bench is too big for the basement egress window and maybe the bench won't fit up the stairs. He told me the reason he's building it down in the basement instead of in the kitchen, but I forget the reason. Take care, Chris

## La rupture du mariage

FROM: Pamela Robinson
TO: Chris Woods

Hi Chris,

God, Patricia sounds unhinged—she sure didn't like you telling her off. But what on earth does she think writing a letter to Mike is going to achieve? For a therapist, Patricia doesn't have much self-awareness does she—you said she never asked about your life, but did you ever tell her you wanted her to? Maybe you could have issued her three fair warning notices, like they do before they sack someone, instead of firing her on the spot . . . too late now though.

I've spoken to Raf—a brief phone call in which he said maybe two words. I wanted to convey to him that my love was unbreakable, and that he could punch it—and me—until the sky broke and still it would stand.

'I know you're upset, Raf,' I said. It was all I could do not to sob.

I heard him breathing.

It sounds ridiculous but I could hear his anguish—his suffering—his regret—rushing through the air. I heard the pulse of his love.

'I know you're hurting,' I said. 'But, Raf, you should never hit anyone. Ever. You need to find a better way of dealing with your anger and pain.'

He hung up.

People get divorced every day—it's the most ordinary thing in the world—but nobody tells you it's like being stabbed in the heart. Today is our wedding anniversary.

I remember exactly what I was doing and where I was when I learned I was going to be divorced. I was standing by a window in a Paris hotel room—we'd rented out our flat and Chris was already living somewhere else. I hadn't seen him since that awful weekend when I'd told him over the phone our marriage was over, and I'd got back to find him gone.

It was a hot afternoon, suffocating, the boys were with some friends of mine at the park—I was about to leave to pick them up. I'd opened a window to let in the air and was standing by the sofa, my back to the window, checking emails on my phone. There was an email from an *avocat* advising me Chris had initiated divorce proceedings. The floor tilted—I fell back on the sofa—I fell out of my life. It had only been a matter of days since I told Chris I no longer loved him. Of course I wanted out! Our marriage was finished, our differences irreconcilable, but I had yet to translate my emotions into words on cold paper—into the legalised death of a marriage that is divorce.

I remember my hands shook as I rang my friends in the park asking if they'd take the boys for the night. The only place I could think to go was to Chris's mother in Deauville. I wasn't thinking straight—I wasn't thinking about anything other than reaching safety. It never even entered my head I might be carrying to her door a terrible burden. I'd known Jacqueline my whole life as a wife, as a parent, she was the closest thing I had to a mother. I didn't think about divorce's divided loyalties—I only knew I loved Jacqueline and she loved me—and Chris, and our children. If I understood that in any division of loyalties, Jacqueline would unhesitatingly stand on her son's side, I also knew she would find it impossible to hate me.

She opened the door and I fell into her arms, everything spilling out in a rush. She ushered me into the kitchen and we read through the dense legal jargon together. The mother of the petitioner—her son, my husband—and me, sobbing quietly over the kitchen table. She'd had no idea. She kept saying, *Je n'en reviens pas, je n'en reviens pas*—she couldn't believe it.

My French deserted me—I couldn't read the text properly. The only words I saw were *la rupture du mariage*. Chris went for the easiest option—*divorce par consentement mutuel*, which required my agreement—allowing us to be divorced within months. If I didn't agree, *divorce pour faute* was threatened—in which some unseen judge would decide who was at fault. How is a judge capable of divining the fault lines inside the average marriage, much less weigh which party should bear the blame? Marriage is a living entity—tidal—veiled even to husband and wife. Who is to weigh its disappointments and mistakes, its myriad acts of hurt and kindness?

Chris and I built our children from our joined bodies—miraculous denouement to that conference of skins, mouths, bones. We created three living beings, as if we were gods. Our sons are our marriage made flesh, the past enshrined, our names forever on record: that one bright day in history—marked every year, forevermore, on this day—a woman named Pamela Rose Robinson, spinster, stood in Woolwich Town Hall and took Christophe Xavier Woods, bachelor, to be her lawful wedded husband. My hair was ringed with flowers, Chris wore a skinny red tie. We ran laughing down the street. Later I disappointed him—later he disappointed me. Isn't that everyone's story?

Oh, Chris, come back! Turn everything to how it was before—everyone together, unabandoned, all five of us in Paris—everlasting!

Love,

Pamela

X

## Truth, again

FROM: Chris Woods

TO: Pamela Robinson

Hi Pamela, I'm going to tell you something you're not going to like. For two years I did volunteer work at a home for teenage mothers. Many were substance abusers. Most were abused, some by parents, but mainly by their partners.

We gave them a crash course in parenting. If they passed, a girl could leave with her baby to start a new life. If she failed, the baby would be taken into foster care or put up for adoption. The question for most girls wasn't whether or not they could learn to care for the baby. It was whether they loved their boyfriend more than their kid.

So, the mom who broke my heart (I had to stop working there) had a long-term abusive boyfriend who harassed her with text messages. *Come back, baby, I swear I'll change. This time it'll be different.* You know, blah blah blah. Lorraine was seventeen years old. She'd already had two kids taken from her. She wanted to make big changes in her life. This time she was desperate to make it work.

We got close. I stayed over some nights, talking to her about her life. She wanted me at the hospital when the baby came, a little girl, underweight. I made sure the doctor let her put the baby against her skin. I lifted Lorraine up so she could slip out of the top of her hospital gown. Lorraine looked up at me and smiled. I thought: *she's going to make it.*

She was fantastic with the baby. She called her Chrisanthi, after me, and she was a terrific mom, responding to her baby's needs, doing everything right.

Then Lorraine started talking about her man, saying she missed him. She showed me his texts, the love heart emoji, the rose emoji. Between feeds, I held Chrisanthi, who snuffled, her head turned blindly towards the sound of her mother's voice. Chrisanthi was nothing but a collection of instincts.

Lorraine kept talking about missing her boyfriend. I kept talking about the consequences of going back to him.

'I know he's no good for me,' she said.

'So, end of story,' I said.

'But I love him! Chris, you don't know how much good he has in him.'

'Where would the good part be located?' I said. 'The part that shook his newborn baby boy? Or the part that punched you in the mouth when you took your son to the doctor?'

She turned away. 'You don't understand.'

'True,' I said.

So, I was left holding Chrisanthi as Lorraine walked out of her daughter's life to go back to her loser of a boyfriend. She couldn't make the emotional break from him. She was like Patricia. She was like Gene. She was like you. Take care, Chris

### Re: Truth, again

FROM: Pamela Robinson
TO: Chris Woods

Oh, Chris, that's unfair. My Chris is not a loser, nor is he abusive—he's a man working with the same flawed human instruments as the rest of us. He wouldn't shake a newborn child! Chris is an imperfect human being with a battered heart, same as mine. What chance for any of us if we fail to join one battered heart to another?

Love,

Pamela

## Dialogue on the Meaning of Salt

FROM: Chris Woods

TO: Pamela Robinson

Dear Plato,

1.  Marriages are mostly left for good reasons. You need to recall the reasons.

2.  The only way to live is forwards. You know what happened to Lot's wife.

Take care, Socrates

### Re: Dialogue on the Meaning of Salt

FROM: Chris Woods

TO: Pamela Robinson

Hi Pamela, everything OK? Haven't heard from you this week.
Take care, Chris

## Hello again

FROM: Pamela Robinson
TO: Chris Woods

Dear Socrates,

I've decided to forgive you. I was so furious I didn't care if I never heard from you again, but these days I've got so many people falling out of my life I can't cope with losing any more—even an invisible person like you.

Deb went home yesterday and today I start back at work after two weeks off—the boys on school holidays for part of it. Deb came with us for a few days in the Blue Mountains. There were log fires and walks and Scrabble games—a stab at normalcy—and all the while an echoing hole left by a missing son. Now I'm lying in bed with my phone, sick at the thought of getting up and going in to work to face everyone.

Deb treated me like an invalid—cups of tea, rugs around my shoulders, cooking for us. For the first few days I couldn't look at her—or anyone—without bursting into tears. My so-called boyfriend has phoned several times offering to help, wanting to come around. He turned up one night unannounced and Deb sent him away. I heard them outside the front door—trying to keep their voices down—talking about me as if I were the lunatic in the attic. 'Nick seems like a sweet guy though,' Deb said when she came inside. 'Maybe just not right now.'

'You can have him,' I said.

'Thanks,' she said. 'I'm sure he'd love to know you just offered him up like scraps from your table.'

I gave her a watery smile. 'I'm sorry. You know I didn't mean it that way.' And then I started crying.

I've forgotten what it's like to feel happy. I long to be the sum of my parts instead of the sum of my sorrows.

Love,

Plato

X

## Sorrows

FROM: Chris Woods
TO: Pamela Robinson

Hi Pamela, everybody's got sorrows. I'll swap sorrows with you. My sorrow is called Patricia. She's letter-bombed the neighbourhood, informing everyone what kind of person I am. Linda at the top of the street calls out when I'm walking by this afternoon. She comes to the gate with a letter from Patricia. 'Are you going to sue?' she says. 'I'd go straight to the cops. Patricia can't go around besmirching your good name. Everyone around here knows you're a good person, Chris.'

The letter is handwritten, with the same words as the letter to Mike, EXCEPT FOR THE MISSING CAPITALS AT THE END. If Patricia's handwritten a letter to every house in our street, her sorrows are hand cramps. Take care, Chris

**Re: Sorrows**

FROM: Pamela Robinson
TO: Chris Woods

Hi Chris,

Well, *are* you going to the police? At least it's not a poison pen letter—she's had the decency to sign her name—so the cops will know where to go. I don't know about you, but I feel tired just thinking about going down that path: the police procedures, the meetings with lawyers—not to mention running into Patricia herself and her volcanic rage. Even from this distance I'm scared of her. I'm so sorry this has happened to you, Chris.

I'm back at work, trying to act like a normal person while covertly inspecting everyone around me—so ordinary, so *normal*. I feel like I'm carrying around a stinking secret, like I'm the only mother on earth who has lost control of her children, and—mortifyingly—I've started to blush like a teenager. I imagine everyone is staring at me; I have lost any notion of how to 'perform' like a normal person. I can't begin to tell you how much these past weeks have unhitched me from all previous knowledge of myself.

I finished work early today for my appointment with Tünde. I sat in her quiet, ordered office, in her quiet, ordered street, picturing beautifully behaved clarinet-playing children making their way home from school to unpack dishwashers for their mothers without being asked—and I wanted to scream. *I know everything I'm supposed to do!* I know I'm supposed to be calm. I know I'm supposed to be the anchor. I know I'm the unyielding rock in the storm that the children must lash themselves to.

Yet, sitting there, the story seemed too long to tell. *Why tell it?* I thought. Anchors, rocks, stories too long to tell—words—written down, here, in a straight line, to you.

Pamela

## Stories

FROM: Chris Woods
TO: Pamela Robinson

Hi Pamela, keep telling me your story. Seems like I'm collecting them. Right now, I'm holed up in the house, so any messages from the outside world are welcome. Mike is walking Mindy, in case I run into Patricia. I caught a glimpse of her yesterday when the girls and Brandon were swimming in the pool. She looked over the fence. I ducked. I'm not going to the cops.

So, my mother wants to move back to Greece. Yeah, you heard me right. 'I want to be buried in my own soil,' she says. My mother can hardly walk to the end of her street. She wants to get on a plane and fly to Athens, make her way to Kalavryta, dust off the family house and move in. There's a framed piece of embroidery hanging in the kitchen, stitched by Mom when she was ten. *It is impossible to escape your fate*, it reads. Mom believes her fate is to die in Kalavryta.

I'm talking to Dora about getting power of attorney. Take care, Chris

## Dying of the truth

FROM: Pamela Robinson
TO: Chris Woods

Hi Chris,

What?? Surely your mother can't move back to Greece at her age. Won't she need a medical certificate declaring her fit to fly? Your mother obviously gains comfort from believing life is governed by fate—personally, I think the whole concept of fate is a story we tell ourselves, in order not to die of knowing we are helpless.

Here's another story for your collection. Today at work I couldn't take my eyes off this woman who came in. She was morbidly obese, all the different parts of her articulated—the great haunch of hip, the poisonous swell of stomach and bum—every bit of her engorged, rolling and rippling. She could only walk at all—with sticks—because of the most superhuman effort. It was suicide by other means, a willed doom, as if by eating the world she was performing a miracle, the transformation of her own suffering, a transubstantiation not of the blood of Christ but of her own pain. She was turning pain to flesh, the invisible into matter.

I suddenly understood the attraction of growing enormously fat or perilously thin—a physical manifestation of human pain. It took every ounce of my self-control not to rush to the table she took so painfully long to reach—the effortful lowering of her enormous bulk into the chair, every part of her engaged—and beg her to tell me everything about her embodied demonstration of suffering. She's given up pretending in fate's story—she's dying of truth in plain sight.

Love,
Pamela

## Re: Dying of the truth

FROM: Chris Woods
TO: Pamela Robinson


Hi Pamela, so, while you're over there trying not to die of truth, I'm over here trying not to murder my mother. Neither Dora nor I can get our crazy mother to change her plans. We can't get power of attorney. I tried two lawyers in Schenectady. No go. Thursday I took the train to see Dora in the city. One of her firm's partners tells us the same thing: if our mother is of sound mind, nothing happening. She has to sign of her own free will. Mom's refusing to sign.

Mike says we should let her move to Greece. 'Why stop her? She wants to go, let her go.'

I say we stop her because she's irresponsible. We stop her because she's doing what she always does, doing whatever she damn well likes with no regard for anyone but herself.

Who's going to be the one moving her out of her apartment? Who's going to be sitting with her on the plane? First, she wants me to go look at carpets. Now she wants me to move with her to Greece. Our family house has been locked up since her last visit ten years ago. It's where we stayed the summer I was eighteen. I haven't been back since. My mother's been back maybe three or four times. It's a house of cobwebs and ghosts. Take care, Chris

## Ghosts

FROM: Pamela Robinson
TO: Chris Woods

Hi Chris,
  Everyone's house is built of cobwebs and ghosts—as St Augustine says, the dead are invisible—they are not absent.
  Much love,
  Pamela

## Re: Ghosts

FROM: Chris Woods
TO: Pamela Robinson

Hey Pamela, I'm the Greek here, remember? It's my crazy Greek mother who gets hysterical if I leave my shoes on their sides because it brings bad luck. Mom wouldn't step over me or Dora when we were kids playing on the floor because it would stunt our growth. We weren't allowed to whistle in the house growing up because it attracted rats. God forbid if one of us whistled at the kitchen table because that brought the devil himself. You think I don't know about ghosts? You think I don't know about the dead hanging from our necks? Us Greeks practically invented dying.

So, ghost house here I come. I've got to let her get on that plane and sit down beside her. This is an old woman who, as a twelve-year-old girl, helped her sister and mother drag her brother's dead body to the cemetery from the hill where he was shot. Every male child over the age of twelve ordered from their home. It's 1943, it might as well be King Herod slaughtering the innocents.

My mother's mother, Yiayia, fussing over Angelo's scarf before he leaves the house. Is he warm enough? Is his coat done up? He has a chill, he's fifteen, the only male in the family. He shouldn't be going into the night air. There's a bad fog, the air is too icy, παγωμένος. He's going outside to get shot and his mother is worried about his chill.

They were shot where they stood. A handful survive under the bodies of the dead. Angelo is not one of them. A few women bury them where they fell, in the frozen ground of December.

Mainly the old women who can't carry them to the cemetery. These are country people from the Peloponnesus, superstitious Greeks, so most of the wives, daughters, mothers and sisters drag the bodies of their husbands, fathers, sons and brothers to the cemetery. To the proper place to be buried. Even though there's no priest left alive to bury them.

Yiayia and Mom and my aunt, Theía Katina, drag Angelo's body on his best winter coat a mile, two miles, three, first making sure his face and hands are wiped clean of blood. There's not a mark on him, my mother says. It appears the blood is not his. Yiayia believes he died of shock. Angelo is so sensitive. Everyone knows he plays the best mandolin of any boy in any village on the Peloponnesus. The story goes: *there was not a mark on him.* So, Angelo becomes the family saint, the boy whose heart stopped before the Germans could shoot him.

Don't tell me about ghosts, Pamela. Don't tell me about angels flying across oceans to land in someone's eyes. Most of all, don't tell me I can't get on a plane with my mother and return her to her village of the dead. I've got to let her get on that plane and sit down beside her. Take care, Chris

## The bodies of children

FROM: Pamela Robinson
TO: Chris Woods

Chris,

I'm not telling you anything—I'm sorry my St Augustine line sounded flippant—it wasn't meant to be. What an appalling story—no wonder your mother is so troubled, so difficult. What parts of her died along with her brother? I read somewhere emotional trauma permeates the body, altering DNA, so the children of trauma victims can genetically inherit trauma too. The bodies of children born decades after famines in Sweden and Holland were found to carry the genetic markers of starvation.

I'm sorry to be complaining about my own small griefs after hearing your mother's story. My boys alive, with their plump lungs; Angelo and those other once-breathing boys in their graves. Take your mother—take her pain—go.

With love,
Pamela
X

198

## Re: The bodies of children

FROM: Chris Woods
TO: Pamela Robinson

Hi again, yeah, well, no-one's leaving the premises yet. Right now the DNA being changed around here is Rima's. I knew something was up last time I went over. She wasn't communicating. No offer of boiled grass tea, no nodding of heads and smiling at each other like we usually do. Now she won't get out of bed.

Rima's stranded in a country that looks wrong. She can't speak the language. Her husband's missing, presumed dead. Her daughters are riding bikes and swimming in pools. She doesn't know yet that one of them has a boyfriend called Brandon.

I went over yesterday and Rima was still in bed. Muaz and I leave her and go sit on the porch. She tells me about their house back home, with a courtyard shaded by vines, where generations of her family lived. The usual sounds in the courtyard were voices and birds. The only noise before they fled was shelling from the streets.

Muaz says Rima misses the house. She wants to go back, Muaz says, even though in the last weeks of living there her mom had to imagine she was already dead to summon the courage to leave the house and go to the market.

Rima tells her they would be better off with Syria's bombs. 'In our culture girls do not go swimming,' Muaz says. 'Girls do not go to college.'

Rima appears to know something else: the full nature of her exile. I'm seeing if one of our Arabic-speaking student counsellors can go see her. We've got plenty at SUNY.

So, yesterday, after visiting Rima and the girls, I go visit Mom, to see if she's still planning on moving to Greece.

I'm inside the door five minutes when she says, 'Look at you. You help a woman who can't speak English before you help your own mother.'

I take a deep breath. 'So, what am I doing now, Mom, over here talking to you?'

She makes that sound, that contemptuous *pffft* noise. At least she doesn't spit. 'I know you, Chrisanthi Xenia,' she says. 'You can't wait to stick your big nose into someone's business.'

Why is she so mean? I'm breathing carefully, trying to picture a girl dragging her brother's dead body on his best winter coat.

'Little Miss Helper,' she says. 'You know what you are, Chrisanthi Xenia?'

'I get the feeling you're gonna tell me, Mom.' I wait for it.

'Είσαι ένα παλιό κοράκι,' she says.

I am an old crow, feasting on other people's disasters.

That's it. I'm up, and out. She's toxic. I forgive her and forgive her and forgive her. I forgive her for making me eat cream cheese out of the trash. I forgive her for not loving me enough, for her disappointment at having a kid who couldn't make her happy. All my life I've been trying to save my mother. I'm supposed to get on that plane, right? I'm a volunteer of love. Take care, Chris

## Volunteer of love

FROM: Pamela Robinson
TO: Chris Woods

Hi Socrates,

You're asking me? The world's leading love expert? Oh, Chris, I don't know. When I was agonising over whether or not to leave Chris, Deb asked me a question: 'It's simple, isn't it? Do you still love him?' But it's not the right question—it's not the defining question, the illuminating question. It won't give you an answer. Of course I loved Chris! I still love him—but I also can't live with him. Love might make you sit next to your mother on the plane—but it might also make you miserable with resentment.

Yours in miserable love,

Plato

X

## Greek sacrifice

FROM: Chris Woods
TO: Pamela Robinson

Hi Plato, well, I guess I'm going. I guess I'm laying down my life like a sacrifice to the gods, a sacrifice at the altar of my mother. We can't get her to sign over power of attorney. We can't get her to change her mind.

It would be great if my mother lost her sense of ownership like that woman in Spain you told me about who forgot what was hers. I'm helping Mom sort through her junk. Why does she keep her last report card from her school in Greece? Why does she keep the crappy glass vase Dora gave her for Mother's Day when Dora was nine? Mom's kept every birthday card she was given. Every medical X-ray, every doctor's letter. Also, every bit of spare paper, string, ribbon, just in case. In case of what? A world shortage of wrapping paper? She's got a tiny, falling-apart piece of Yiayia's wedding crown, for Pete's sake. She's like a deranged Greek Miss Havisham.

It's not like I haven't been through this before. I spent months packing up the family house when she moved into St Sophia's. Mom keeps her world on her back, like a snail. She's like one of those hoarders they discover dead under piles of newspapers. My instinct is to pay someone to take the lot to the trash. Except that would be like removing her skin. Mom thinks this physical debris is *her*. She thinks she's in there somewhere.

So, I find a picture of the three of them—Yiayia, Mom, my aunt—standing on the quay in Piraeus, holding hands. They're ready to leave on a ship for America. Mom sees me looking at the photograph.

'We thought gold flowed from the taps in America,' she says. 'The three of us held hands as we left our homeland. I believed the three of us would be holding hands when we returned.'

I've spent my life trying to turn myself into those missing hands. Take care, Socrates

## Breathing

FROM: Pamela Robinson
TO: Chris Woods

Hi Chris,

Isn't it extraordinary that we can't perceive the knots of our own lives but think we see—fully lit—the tangles of others? Surely you don't need me to tell you that you'll never be those missing hands—that you can help me and Muaz and Rima and Tracey and every drowning woman in the world till your hands bleed, but Mrs Calliope Pappas will remain a sad woman who dragged her brother's body over frozen ground.

Look at us! You packing up a life—me trying to piece our lives back together. Why isn't my own life fully lit? Why am I blundering around in fathomless black? Raf's still at Ben's house—it's just me and Claude and Baps. I spend as much time as I can sitting quietly with Baps, cuddling him or playing with him and Souris. The small cat crouching under the couch—me and Baps squealing with our legs up, one of us leaning over every now and then to put a fingertip on the floor for Souris to swipe. I need to hear Bap's laugh—I need the cat to be waiting under the couch for us to offer a finger, the friendly swat of his soft paw with its claws withdrawn.

I can't open my mouth these days without offending Claude. He's sick of doing his hand exercises. 'I'm doing them!' he shouts when I remind him, then slams the door to his bedroom so I can't see if he's doing them correctly or not. Even when I ask a desultory, non-inflammable question—if he's remembered his sports bag or whether he has the right money for an excursion—he shouts, 'Don't talk to me about school all the time!'

I drive him to school every morning now—past the Fake Grass House—to ensure I see him physically walk in the gates. Some mornings I get a text even before my first coffee to say he's been marked absent. Then I nick out from work—I'm running out of reasons to excuse myself—and drive around looking for him. I never find him.

This morning at breakfast I tried to talk to him about his absences. But before I could even get a word out he shouted, 'Stop breathing over my food!' and rushed from the room.

Maybe it will help everyone if I stop breathing.

Love,

Pamela

X

### Re: Breathing

FROM: Chris Woods
TO: Pamela Robinson

Plato, you are the lungs of the family. Keep breathing. Here in Schenectady I'm breathing the air of fall. The summer clothes are in the loft. Mike has covered the pool. The air's got winter in it. Every fall, a day comes when panic grips my throat. I think of the coming snow, the way cold prowls the city like an attack dog. I don't know how I managed to live in Schenectady my whole life. Take care, Socrates

## Suffering

FROM: Pamela Robinson
TO: Chris Woods

Hi Chris,

I haven't seen Raphael for eight weeks. I've met Marion—the mother of his friend Ben—several times but whenever I drop in, Raf's either not at home, or off in a room somewhere, studying. I think I told you she's a school guidance officer? She's arranged for Raf to see a psychologist specialising in adolescents but the advice of Raf's psychologist, conveyed through Marion, is that he should be the one to decide when contact between us is resumed. Besides being devoured by anxieties about Raf—how he is, how he's coping, whether we'll ever have a relationship again—I'm worried about what he's saying to the psychologist about my failed parenting. I have no idea what he's said to Marion either and she's incredibly discreet. I can't ask.

Every Monday I drop off the $100 a week I'm paying Marion for Raf's upkeep. Her house has a whispery quiet—all polished floorboards, statues of Buddha, scented candles. First, you remove your shoes at the door. There's a cosy nook in a corner of the living room where we sit while she pours me green tea—low seats covered in richly coloured Indian throws, screened off with some sort of Balinese screen, and a wooden fan clicking softly overhead. It's like being in a monastery or a retreat—peaceful, calm, there's even the sound of water trickling (I assume the sound comes from an unseen pond with sleek golden carp swimming through it rather than a dripping tap). I keep hoping I'll see Raf.

'Raphael's a lovely boy—a gentle soul,' Marion said yesterday.

It took every shred of self-control not to shout, *I know he's a lovely boy! He's MY lovely boy, who once lay like a miracle in the cave of my body. Give him back!* I didn't trust myself to speak.

'How are you coping?' she asked.

My eyes hurt from held-back tears. I could only nod.

This is a picture of a mother being told it is up to her child to decide when they should speak again. What is the Nature of Suffering?

Much love,

Pamela

## Dialogue on the Nature of Suffering

FROM: Chris Woods

TO: Pamela Robinson

Hi Plato,

1.   The New Jerusalem of no tears and no pain, of no mourning and no death, has not arrived.

2.   A grieving woman goes to Buddha with the dead body of her son, begging him to bring her son back to life. She cannot bear a second longer the burden of her suffering. Sure, says Buddha, sure I can do that. First you need to bring back a mustard seed from every house you visit where no-one has known death. The mother's so happy. She tenderly lays the body down, rushes out to knock on the first door she comes to. No luck: the husband just died. The next house, a grandmother buried the month before. Same with the next house, and the next. Every house she comes to has known death. After she's knocked on every house in the village, and every single house has known death, she gets it. How many doors do you have to knock on?

Socrates

## Doors

FROM: Pamela Robinson
TO: Chris Woods

Dear Socrates,

How many doors? I don't know—a hundred? A million? I'm knocking on every door of every house in the world until I find the door which opens onto relief. But while I'm out knocking on doors, someone's knocking on mine—Nick Waterman.

*Go away*, I wanted to scream. Instead—being terminally female and trained never to hurt the feelings of men—I said, *Look, now's not a good time, Nick. Maybe later?* I said, *I can't handle a relationship at the moment. I've got too much on my plate.* Actually, I wanted to scream, *Fuck off!*

Of course I can't handle a relationship! I can't handle the relationship I have with my own children, let alone one with a new man.

'Let's have coffee. No pressure. I want to help, babe. We don't have to have a "relationship".' He made quote marks in the air. 'Can't we be friends?'

The answer to that is I have all the friends I need—and I've yet to meet a man for whom friendship is not a Trojan horse. Nick wants to help with the boys—kick a ball with them, take them fishing. He'll babysit one night if I want, so Deb and I can go out on the town. I need to go out on the town like I need a boyfriend. Especially one who calls me 'babe'.

Claude had his last physio appointment, thank God. His hand has healed—there's just the faintest trail of puckered skin running down one side of his finger. He told me the tip of his little finger feels slightly numb, but he doesn't want me looking at it anymore. I thought: *His stitches may have disappeared but his body will remember.* All the while the first frangipani buds of spring are opening. The jasmine's out, the trees frilled and the air sparkling, a new green world everywhere in burst and bloom—except at the Fake Grass House, where the seasons are permanently arrested.

Love,
Plato
X

## The Ratfink

FROM: Chris Woods
TO: Pamela Robinson

Hi Pamela, yeah, well, falling leaves are clattering like bones around these parts. Dead leaves, dead people. Still helping Mom sort her dead. Today I found a photograph of my dad I've never seen before. He's a teenager, about to leap into a river, one arm flung back. The photographer must have been low on the ground, maybe lying on it. No-one in Evrostina owned a camera in 1921. I see on the back it was taken by a photographer from Athens.

'The day I married The Ratfink, my miserable life away from my beloved homeland began,' says Mom, looking over my shoulder. 'He was a playboy. No good.' Mom never calls my dad anything except The Ratfink.

Mom's five uncles had stitched up most of Albany and Schenectady by the time she arrived in New York. Hotels, laundries, cafes and restaurants. It started with two Matsoukis brothers emigrating in 1906 (Matsoukis is Mom's family name; Pappas is her married name).

The story goes the uncles' wives are so jealous of the two beautiful young virgins arrived from Greece, they want them married off and out of the house ASAP. They don't have green cards, they can only stay three months. So, Mom and Theía Katina and Yiayia go across the border into Canada to await re-entry. While they are there they take a few English classes.

In class Katina meets a handsome young Frenchman on a Canadian work permit. They fall in love. They want to get married. I guess by then Yiayia's world has disappeared: her son is dead, her old life gone. Everywhere is ξένος, foreign. What does it matter to her if one of her daughters marries a strange man in another strange country? The marriage turns out to be happy. When Katina and Jean-Claude retire they kiss goodbye to their kids in Canada and move back to Jean-Claude's home town of Fitou in southern France. They live out the rest of their days in the sun drinking wine they make from their own grapes. I went to visit them in France when I was eighteen.

Mom gets the unhappy marriage and The Ratfink. My father was sixty-two when I was born. Mom was twenty-one. He'd already had one wife. His first wife ran off because he was a drinker and a gambler, the family black sheep. His family hoped a sacrificial virgin would turn him into a lamb. It turned him into a wife beater.

The Ratfink died when I was eight and Dora is four. She doesn't remember him. You know the last thing he said to me? 'You fat bitch.' He comes into my bedroom, his last night on earth, and I push him away. I don't mean he tried to sexually assault me, God forbid. He was trying to give me a beery kiss goodnight. He was a drunken oaf, overflowing with the love of humanity when he'd had one too many. He cried listening to Nat King Cole's 'When I Fall in Love'. (It's ruined Nat King Cole for me forever.)

So there I am, crying in my little bed because my pop's just called me a fat bitch. Mom comes in, starts shouting, shoos him out.

The next day he dies. I think I've killed him. I believe my hate has formed itself into a magical force that strikes his heart, stopping it stone dead. I'm holding Mom's hand at his funeral, the good little girl who doesn't cry, trying to turn myself into Caroline Kennedy, the reason for my mother to live again.

I remember Mom saying to me that night, 'My golden adventure to the USA is over. The Ratfink ruined my life.' Maybe she doesn't say it that same night. In my memory, she does.

After that, Mom works in Matsoukises' laundry every hour God sends us. I am in charge of getting dinner after school. I am in charge of Theodora doing her homework, getting her to Greek school on time on Saturdays.

I see that photograph of my dad and it may as well be a photograph of me. I look exactly like The Ratfink. His name was Konstantinos Pappas. Take care, Chris

## Standing like angels

FROM: Pamela Robinson
TO: Chris Woods

Hi Chris,

How I wish I could see that photograph of The Ratfink. I love old photographs, even when I don't know anybody in them. I love seeing time stilled, an emotion caught, a splash from time's endless river—the days lit, standing like angels. What is a photograph but a miracle of light and time? A single day—still standing—surrounded by annihilating time.

On my dressing table I've got a yellowed black-and-white photograph of my grandmother's brother, David—dead at twenty-one, killed in France in 1917. A young man from Orange, New South Wales, who had never been to Sydney before he left for the other side of the world. He's maybe ten or eleven, standing in the back row with five other boys, four boys sitting on a bench in front of them. Every boy in the photograph is dressed as a country bumpkin's idea of a London toff in the early twentieth century—top hats and tails, buttoned waistcoats, bow ties. Each boy carries a cane, and every boy's right eye is ringed with a black circle to simulate a monocle.

There's David at the back, instantly recognisable because he looks so much like my father. He's the only boy with an incipient smile challenging his lips, his cardboard top hat at a perilous angle. Life's bursting from him—energy, movement—he looks as if he's ready to jump from the frame. Too soon the camera is downed, the eye closes, the boys throw off their top hats, their tails, drop their canes in the grass as they rush towards their futures—how many to die in France? All of them?

Empire is the name of the postcard maker on the back—there's no writing, no stamp—and on the front a stilled image of wriggling, future ghosts. Light, time and silence.

Send me a photograph of *you* before you are a ghost in time. A photograph is better than nothing—I'm still longing to meet you, to sit down over coffee or wine and talk and talk and talk. On a fine day you can show me Schenectady's disintegrating parks and we can speak long and quietly and with heart. How quickly our emails have come to seem like friendship distilled to its essence. Is friendship the wrong word? Maybe it is. Communication between souls then—or dialogue at its most pure. There's too much noise in the world—too much commotion—but here, in this silent space, devoid of our bodies, there's a quiet chamber for reflection. I don't have conversations like this with anyone—not even with Deb. Can people be friends in the absence of their bodies? And what function do I serve that your embodied friends don't?

Love,
Pamela
X

## Friends with bodies

FROM: Chris Woods
TO: Pamela Robinson

Hi Pamela, like I said, no photograph. Ever. What function do you serve that my friends with bodies don't? No buried envy or unspoken competitiveness maybe? That's kind of a joke (I think). My best friend lives in Atlanta, Georgia. Vicky and I met in Greek school a million years ago. I hardly ever see her now. She's got five kids. Her husband George (he's Greek too) works in radio. When we were young we used to stalk him. He was a big radio star, kind of a heartthrob. We both had crushes on him. So, Vicky got him, not me. Am I happy he's run to fat? Yes. Vicky sometimes emails. She goes on about the brilliance of her kids. Her big house, her vacations in the Bahamas. I kind of lost the race.

My other friends are from work. Becky, Letitia, Tracey with the incompetent cervix. We go to the movies. We go eat. I've been to Letitia's house, and Becky's. Tracey's kind of weird; skinny and wired. She talks in that new way girls talk, low and growly. I think maybe a Kardashian started it.

Back when Vicky and I were teenagers stalking George, he rang me up. Vicky and I hung around the radio studio, pouncing on George the moment he came out. We bombarded him with notes with our telephone numbers, never imagining he would ever ring. Lucky it was me who answered the phone and not Mom.

I met him at a bar. The legal drinking age back then was nineteen. No way on God's earth I looked nineteen. The bartender didn't bat an eye. Probably he'd seen young girls with George before.

The whole time I'm sitting in that booth, drinking my soda, I'm thinking: *George chose me!* My heart was doing a war dance: *Me! Me! Me!* Not real Christian, huh.

Nothing happened. I was fifteen years old, a good Greek girl. I got scared out of my wits, and when he tried to kiss me I ran home on my fat little legs.

Did I tell Vicky about it? Of course. I watched her pretty face fall, my victorious pleasure straight away turning to shame that I had hurt her. 'Nothing happened, Vicky! I swear!'

Was that the end of it? It was not. When I was twenty-two, just before they got married, I ran into George when he was on a trip home to Schenectady. He'd already moved to Atlanta; Vicky was following him down after the wedding.

He asked me out for a drink. I was engaged to Mike. George was marrying Vicky. Why not have a drink? Four Manhattans later is why not. Four Manhattans and an embrace in a back lane is why not. So, I'm kissing my best friend's fiancé, he wants us to get a hotel room, and what's the only thing going through my head? *He wants me! Me!* Are you sure you still want to meet me in the flesh Plato? Take care, Chris

## The first stone

FROM: Pamela Robinson
TO: Chris Woods

Hi Chris,

Well, he who casts the first stone and all that. Yes, I still want to meet you—I have no husband left to kiss, so we should be fine. I need to prove you're real—that you're not a hole in the air.

Much love,

Pamela

X

## A hole in the air

FROM: Chris Woods
TO: Pamela Robinson

Hi Pamela, I guess the truth is I don't want to meet you. I like being a hole in the air. Why wreck dreaming with reality? I like being a character in someone's head. I can be anyone. To be honest, our emails are kind of a vacation. A break from dragging my sorry butt around, from driving to and from work, feeding the dog and the cat, cooking dinner. A break from keeping my head down when I can't avoid walking past Patricia's house. Why spoil the fun? Take care, Chris

## Questions

FROM: Pamela Robinson
TO: Chris Woods

Hi Chris,

I've got to admit there's much about your life that's baffling to me. I feel like I've laid myself bare, but there's some secret at your centre—some vast, untraversed hinterland behind your words. I don't understand why you're not home more with your husband—sitting companionably with Mike and your trembling dog and your three-legged cat—instead of out saving every woman and girl on the planet. Doesn't Mike mind? What does he think about you taking your mother to Greece? *Are* you still taking her to Greece? You haven't said anything about him going too. So many questions.

With love,

Pamela

X

## Re: Questions

FROM: Chris Woods
TO: Pamela Robinson

Hi Pamela, I don't do reflection. I don't want to be rude, but you do enough reflection for the entire population of Australia. There's a fine line between reflection and self-indulgence.

You want the real me? My dark secrets? I love my house. I love my husband. I love all food except liver and kidneys. I've got a small scar on my forehead from where I fell off a motorbike in Greece when I was eighteen.

I prefer summer to winter. *Madame Bovary* is my favourite book. I speak bad Greek, a Greek spoken in a mountain village fifty years ago. I like colour, so Mike painted every room in our house a different shade. We have a red wall in the kitchen. Our bathroom is painted Greek blue.

I believe in God. I don't go to church. I think of myself as an independent Christian, not the loudmouth born again, hallelujah, proselytising type of holy roller.

Come on, Pamela. Who knows who anybody is? You said so yourself: we hardly know our own selves. Yeah, I'm still taking Mom to Greece. Mike is not coming. He prefers home. Take care, Chris

## Reflection

FROM: Pamela Robinson
TO: Chris Woods

Hi Chris,

You think I don't know my endless reflecting is insufferable—not only to you, but especially to my ex-husband? Over-thinking is the only kind of thinking I have! At first Chris might have loved my unruly heart and over-thinking head, but how quickly they became the very things he couldn't stand. If he started out wanting to eat my excessive heart to acquire its powers like a cannibal, he soon found the taste made him gag.

I was talking about this with Tünde. Our story is out—on the table, spilled on the floor—and I walk around it, week after week. There it is—our small catastrophe—our map of the war. In Tünde's calm, polished office it's like a bloodstain on the carpet—I sit in her expensive chair leaking like a wound. I'm trying to gather us up, every shredded bit of us: blood, tears—who can tell?

Tünde suggests my reflecting head seems to run around the same circular track. She says endless rumination on the past might even be a form of suffering I'm choosing. 'It seems to me you're getting something out of it,' she said.

I looked at her, perplexed. 'Like what?'

'Perhaps over-thinking is a way of protecting yourself from something. You seem to be holding very tightly to your pain.'

I've already told her about forgetting to laugh. I've already said my sense of humour has run off, so that when I'm sitting playing with Baps, pretending to laugh, all I hear is this gro-tesque pantomime *ha, ha, ha*.

'It's protecting me from a good night's sleep,' I said. *Ha, ha, ha*.

'Is that all?' she asked.

For the life of me I can't understand what she's getting at. All I want is for this endless rumination to stop! As if I need this ceaseless pain—this dreadful new life I wake to day after day.

At home, I've followed Tünde's stern advice to the letter—I have clear house rules pinned to the fridge for Baps and Claude to follow. The Xbox has left the building. School laptops are used at the kitchen table, and then only under supervision. Each evening Claude and Baps and I gather for dinner like newly shorn puritans.

And every night I fail to get Claude to understand he cannot bunk off school. I've told him his head of year called to say his unexplained absences were getting perilously close to the maximum number any student is allowed before he is suspended.

'Mr Cameron's worried,' I said. 'He said he can't afford to lose his player.' Claude loves soccer.

'I can't play, Mum,' he said. His hand accident has side-lined him.

'Not this season. But you can soon if you don't get suspended. Claude, it's vital you don't miss any more school.'

I understand from Tünde that I must act as if life as we knew it has not ended—I should pretend we are not fallen from the sky to strangeness. But I also know that, for the moment at least, Raphael no longer lives with us and Claude's 'real' friends are far away—and so is his father. Everyone in our house—and Raphael over at Marion's—lives with this estrangement. I don't understand where Tünde expects us to put our pain. If she tells me, I'll be the first to lay it down.

With love,

Pamela

X

## Suffering

FROM: Chris Woods
TO: Pamela Robinson

Hi Pamela, I'll send you a birch stick so you can beat yourself up some more. You never know, I might find one among Mom's debris. We sent two boxes ahead to Greece. Mom's on the phone day and night to the family looking after the ghost house. Gregoria someone who married a Marenty from Skepasto, who has that son who is Theía Matsoulis's cousin who married Uncle George's daughter, Chrysanthi Matsoukis. Families in Greece are like road maps: every damn person knows exactly which donkey track leads to the main road.

I wonder how many days Mom has left on this earth. I'm wondering if she takes after her father, who died young. Or if she takes after Yiayia, who was ninety-eight when she died, lost to dementia. Mom's still going strong so I guess she takes after Yiayia.

Mom spends her days shouting down the phone in Greek, bellowing instructions to Gregoria someone about getting the telephone and internet connected at the ghost house. Every conversation, she says, in Greek, 'My time in the USA is over. I am returning to live out the rest of my days in my beloved homeland.' She sounds like a broken record.

When I was eighteen, the ghost house had no running water. Mom had a bathroom put in during her last visit. When I was there you got water from the well. There was no phone, and definitely no internet. No Socratic email dialogue for you and me back then. I'd be like a goat stranded on a Greek mountain. You'd be writing letters in longhand beating yourself up. Take care, Chris

## The birch stick

FROM: Pamela Robinson
TO: Chris Woods

Hi Chris,

I wish I was going with you—flying away. I'm tired of staying on the same hard old ground. You should see Tünde's instructing me in the art of making better choices than the birch stick, how to fold myself like emotional origami. Take one anxiety here—wrap it in. A wild, escaping lock of emotion—fold it back.

I'm telling her stories—about Baps sleeping in my bed, about my desire to keep him safe and ungrown; about the Fake Grass House, its seasons arrested, time stopped. I tell her about a flower I see every day on my walk to work (I'm no longer driving Claude—he has to learn it's his responsibility to get himself to school). The flower has fallen from a frangipani overhanging the street which I've been admiring as I pass: most usually the creamy yellow and white flowers are artfully arranged among the leaves like so many bouquets. Every morning I've been turning up my head to inhale their perfume, but one morning this week I saw a single flower, caught on a solitary strand of spider web running from the frangipani tree to a bottlebrush on the other side of the footpath, the spun thread barely visible, so that the flower seemed pinned to the sky, suspended in air above my head like a miracle. It was abandoned in time—captured eternally falling.

I think the flower is trying to tell me something.

Love,

Pamela

X

## Flowers

FROM: Chris Woods

TO: Pamela Robinson

Hi Pamela, the last time a flower tried to tell me something was in Greece. I was on the roof of the ghost house, the vines hanging, the stones beneath my feet still warm. I can smell the summer heat, food cooking in the kitchen. A bright pink bougainvillea flower fell on my head. If there was a moment I passed for pretty, that was it.

I'm trying to picture myself there now. Last time I was in Kalavryta the local shop had just started stocking sanitary napkins. What the women and girls did before that I do not know. Now it's got everything. I googled the main street. It's tourist heaven. There's probably a Starbucks.

Still laying low in Schenectady. Take care, Chris

## Raphael

FROM: Pamela Robinson
TO: Chris Woods

Hi Chris,

I've seen Raphael. Marion told me last time I went around that Raf was ready to meet me. Through Marion we arranged to talk at a cafe near her place—just the two of us. I got there early and didn't know what to do with my hands. I had my smartphone—the people's friend—so I pretended to check emails, looked at Facebook, scrolled through Instagram, though I was so nervous I couldn't read or see anything. The entire time I was pretending to look at my phone, I was really watching the door.

He came in ten minutes late. Raphael! It hurt just looking at him—his face so like Scotty's. I didn't throw my arms around his neck, although I wanted to. I waited for him to see me, my heart jumping. When his eyes finally settled on me sitting in a far corner, he blushed. I smiled at him.

'*Bonjour*, Maman,' he said when he reached me.

I stood up, gave him an awkward hug across the table. 'Hello, love.'

He arranged himself in a chair, a newly giant man, so recently a boy. His hair had grown—no more buzz cut—his blond curls are back and he looked softer, younger, and more vulnerable.

'What do you want? Juice? A hot drink?'

He picked up the menu. While he read it I measured the calibrations of his loved face, those measurements belonging to no-one else on earth but Raf.

A young waitress came over, both arms covered in sleeve tattoos. 'Can I get a Coke, please,' Raf said. He knows I don't let him drink Coke.

I wasn't supposed to ask how he was—Tünde advised me not to pepper him with questions, saying that I should leave it to him to lead the conversation. We sat in silence for several long minutes, me catching his eye now and then. Did I start out wanting to talk to him about the various ways terror expresses itself through the body? That men—and boys—can feel frightened and abandoned and terrified out of their wits but fear should never fly from their hands? If Raphael had failed to learn this cardinal lesson growing up, how was I going to cram an accelerated domestic violence program into him now? When it became clear he wasn't going to speak, I began.

'Look, Raf, we don't need to talk about what happened,' I said. 'Though we do need to discuss it at some point. Right now, the main thing you need to know is that I love you.'

He looked down at the table. He looked at the wall, at a photograph above my head, he looked everywhere but at me. He nodded.

We sat in more silence, stranded with our love. How hard it is to speak deep and true! Panicked questions rushed through my head: *How did your exams go, are you eating properly, how are we ever going to right this appalling moment which has befallen us?* It was so difficult not to rush to fill that yawning space—to place words in it—*any* words—as if words could ever fill the terrible gap between us. I felt as if everyone was looking at us—a mother and a son, mute, at a table. Raf and me—enough love between us to fill heaven—but helpless before it. We drank our drinks, noted the time. I started to say how much better Claude's hand was before I realised where that subject led to—God help me—so I talked instead about Bap and Souris's latest adventures.

'Souris has a new trick,' I said. 'He clings to the back of the sofa and—'

'I got two As,' Raf said, interrupting.

'Oh, Raf, that's wonderful!' I said, remembering just in time to hose down my enthusiasm. 'That'll set you up so well for next year. In which subjects?'

'French and art,' he said.

I asked about the French exam—I told him I was hopeless at art myself—I told him my best subject was ancient history—I told him I'd like to take him out to dinner to celebrate . . . I may have accidentally gabbled.

Oh, Chris, it was inexpressibly sad, but—oh!—a shiver of grace!

With love,
Pamela
X

## Re: Raphael

FROM: Chris Woods
TO: Pamela Robinson

Hi Pamela, that's great you saw your son. Great to hear you understand you have to speak to Raphael sometime about him hitting you. The sooner the better in my opinion. A shiver of grace is all very well but a stern lecture comes in handy.

So, Patricia not only wrote to Mike, to Linda at the top of the street and every other house in Hampton Avenue, she wrote to my boss at SUNY, Mr Bedford. He should know the kind of woman he employs. It's handwritten, naturally, but this time Patricia adds a twist. I am sly as well as passive aggressive.

Mr Bedford calls me into his office. 'Tell me about this Patricia person,' he says. I tell him. After I explain, Mr Bedford says, 'OK, we won't call the cops if you don't want.' I've worked here a long time, only one person ever complained about me. Some looney tunes mom who thought I was influencing her daughter too much.

'Maybe leave off the Florence Nightingale act for a while,' he says. 'Lie low.'

As I'm exiting Mr Bedford's office, I can tell he is thinking differently about me. Mud sticks. No smoke without fire etc.

I'm thinking: I should go over to Patricia's to confront her. Or maybe that will make things worse. Maybe I can write her a letter. Drop it in her letterbox like she dropped her letter to Mike in mine. I'm thinking about what I should write. I should apologise. That's what she wants. But every time I think about apologising, smoke comes out my ears.

I'm praying for guidance. God is answering, *Chrisanthi, that woman is a nut.* Take care, Chris

## Life Lessons 101

FROM: Pamela Robinson
TO: Chris Woods

Hi Chris,

Maybe the time's arrived to go to the police. Can you get a restraining order on a letter writer? Surely it's a criminal offence of some sort. Maybe it's a form of stalking? Or it might be defamation—I don't know. Whatever it is, it's a pain in the arse. You must be furious.

According to Tünde in Life Lessons 101, though, everyone has a choice as to how they respond to any situation. 'There's always a space between an event and our response to it. We have the power to choose our response, Pamela,' she said in our last session. 'You can't avoid loss—none of us can—but you can choose how you respond to it.' I'm thinking: *Try telling that to— oh, I don't know—a woman whose daughter's been murdered, or a father whose kid has drowned.* How can anyone—Chrisanthi Woods, for instance, in response to Patricia's letter-bombing— pause for a quiet reflective moment to choose empathy or fury from an array of emotions laid out like so many different-col- oured ties? I say smoke comes out your ears quicker than you can pick a tie.

I've got to admit, Tünde's irritating the hell out of me: so composed and calm and chillingly perfect—everything I'm not. I'm being mauled by the dogs of chaos and there she sits, calm as a mountain. I want to tie her to a chair and ransack her office, find out everything about her—the secret to her happy family, how any fucking family is supposed to function. I feel the most alarming violence watching her straight expensive bob fall in a perfect line an inch above her shoulders. Her plain, intelligent face eschews the flirtations of lipstick. She's *very* unsmiley—refusing to ease any tension, declining to take up the female role of making everyone feel at home. Of course I know it's not her job to make me feel like a welcome guest at a dinner party. Of course I know she doesn't need to like me and I don't need to like her—she's not my friend. But I've read Primo Levi, for God's sake! I know that even something as obliterating as the Holocaust requires a decision—that everyone in the face of despair must choose to fall or rise. I know there's a decision to make about how much to remember—without dying of remembering.

Love,
Pamela

## Choosing a tie

FROM: Chris Woods
TO: Pamela Robinson

Hi Pamela, how many emotions do we get to choose from? My fury tie is getting a little thin. I'm not sure which one to pick for my big new problem. Maybe the oh-my-God-what-have-I-done tie.

Muaz and Zahiya's mom Rima is getting worse. She found out about Brandon. She's no longer talking. Rima has seen three different Arabic-speaking counsellors. A social worker. She won't take medication. Even the evil twin can't get her mom out of bed. She's fading away.

'She does not like America,' says Muaz. I kind of guessed that.

The last few times I was over I sat by Rima's bed, holding her hand, looking into her sad eyes. She's so thin.

Yesterday I go around, Muaz is out at her accelerated math class (turns out she's super bright) and Zahiya is by Rima's bed, trying to spoonfeed her mother. 'Mama, Mama, you must eat,' Zahiya is saying. 'Eat!' She says it first in Arabic, then in English, for my benefit I suppose. I'm sitting by the bed too, holding Rima's hand. I take the bowl of rich-smelling soup from Zahiya, try to spoonfeed Rima myself.

'Go do your homework,' I say to Zahiya. 'Rima, you need to eat. Your daughter is right.'

Rima takes one spoonful, wipes her mouth, shakes her head. No more, no more. Even I understand that.

Zahiya is frightened. Rima *is* Syria, home. She is their lost life. Their mom is their vanished father. God forbid anything should happen to her. I put the soup down, hold her hand, willing her to rise.

Then I hatch a plan. 'Zahiya, come here, honey.'

Zahiya comes over. 'Tell your mom I'm ordering her to get better. Tell her that unless she gets up to guide you into Allah's light, peace be upon him, you and Muaz will be cast into darkness.'

Zahiya looks shocked.

'Tell her that please, Zahiya. Word for word. Tell her that unless she rises to teach you the words of the Holy Quran, the USA will corrupt you.'

'I can't say that!' she cries. 'It is her greatest fear!'

Muaz is not home. Do you think I'd try my little trick if that firecracker was around?

'Go on, Zahiya. Say it. Can you remember the exact words? That unless she rises to teach you the words of the Holy Quran, the USA will corrupt you. Go on!'

Zahiya looks at me. 'I can't.'

'Yes, you can. We need to get your mom out of bed.'

While this is going on, Rima is looking from my face to Zahiya's, back and forth, increasingly worried.

'It's our only hope, Zahiya.'

Zahiya looks at her mom, takes a breath, and then says something in Arabic. Rima's eyes widen. 'Now say the next bit. Unless she gets up to guide you into Allah's light, peace be upon him, you and Muaz will be cast into darkness. Got that?'

Zahiya speaks again. Rima sits up, starts speaking fast in Arabic. She starts howling into her hands. I'm thinking, *Maybe my plan was crap.*

Zahiya starts crying. 'Oh, Mrs Woods, what have you done?'

Rima is howling now.

Right at that moment, the evil twin walks in the door. 'Mom! What's going on?' She rushes across to the bed.

Zahiya rattles off something in Arabic, Rima's sobbing. I'm sitting there like a schmuck.

'Mrs Woods! I am ashamed of you!' Muaz yells at me over the racket. 'We thought you were our dear friend!'

'I am your dear friend. I'm only trying to help.'

'How is this help? Telling our mother her greatest terrors will come true?'

Zahiya's crying now, Rima's wailing, Muaz is looking like she wants to kill me.

'Well, I guess I'll I leave you to it,' I say, like the arsonist who drops a match and races home to watch the fire on TV.

I don't give a hoot how many letters Patricia writes to other people trashing my name. I only care about the girls and their mom. Take care, Chris

## Anger

FROM: Pamela Robinson
TO: Chris Woods

Hi Chris,

God, how will you get out of this one? I have no idea which tie will help you now. I only hope your high-risk do-it-yourself psychology manoeuvre works—that instead of applying electric shock treatment to Rima's distraught head, you've shocked her another way. I'm not sure if using religious anxieties to galvanise a wretched woman into rising from her bed is quite the thing—but what would I know? I can't begin to imagine the dimensions of Rima's losses.

I see loss and grief everywhere I look. I went out for a drink with everyone from work last night—it was someone's birthday and I haven't had a drink after work in ages. If I was trying to impersonate a normal, cheery person, I ended up turning into Attila the Hun wanting to kill everyone. I left in a rage without even finishing my drink. The whole evening went badly from the start. Straight away I got into a conversation with a colleague who told me one of her kid's best friends had just died—he'd turned seventeen the week before—he had leukaemia. 'We're *so* lucky,' she said. 'We've never had anything like that in our family.'

Is it only other people who get cancer? Only other people who live on the wrong side of luck? I didn't stop to pick a tie—I immediately turned into my seething father.

'You really believe that? An educated woman like you? That luck runs in families?'

She looked startled—taken aback by my vehemence.

I stepped closer. 'The older I get the more I believe every one of us is only a breath away from collapse,' I said. 'Accidents, disease, job loss, divorce. The whole concept of safety is an illusion.'

She looked at me with something resembling pity.

'Oh, come on, Kate,' I went on. 'Don't be such a Pollyanna.'

'And don't be such a pessimist,' she said. 'Not everyone has bad luck like you, Pamela.'

I haven't breathed a word about Raf! About his court appearance, or why he moved out. I haven't told anyone about our fight—or Claude's hand—or that I am seeing a therapist once a week in order to stay upright. As far as I'm aware the only thing Kate knows about my personal life is that I'm divorced.

'Is getting divorced bad luck?'

She looked uncomfortable, as if she would prefer to be talking to anyone else but me.

'Divorce isn't catching, as far as I know,' I went on, 'if that's what you're worried about.' I was suddenly furious—I *do* think divorce is catching: it makes people examine the fault lines in their own marriages. And I was full of rage—towards wilfully stupid women; towards everyone in the world who stays married knowing full well they are married to deception.

'Of course I know divorce isn't catching,' Kate said. 'Some people are lucky to stay married till the end.'

I couldn't believe my ears—as well as believing herself inoculated by luck against cancer, Kate believes she's inoculated against divorce. She thinks she and her husband are permanent stones— statues in the Arundel Tomb, side by side, their mortal bones rendered immortal through marriage's holy sacraments. She's Catholic, a proper practising one, which means only the Pope can annul her union before God. God married her—God himself!

I'm sorry if I'm being blasphemous, Chris—but for fuck's sake!

'What a load of bullshit!' I said. 'You could go home and find your husband with his bags packed. You could walk out the door and get cancer. No-one has eternal good luck.'

She looked hard at me. 'And divorce doesn't turn everyone bitter and twisted like you either.'

She walked away.

I stood with my mouth open like a gasping fish. If there are five stages to grieving, I'm at the anger stage—the stage that wants to shoot stupid, smug women with their endless good luck—the stage that wants to roar from the rooftops that I've been wronged—that my life wasn't meant to turn out this way—that someone lied to me about love conquering all. I feel like I'm ready to spontaneously combust, as if all the anger in all the world is gathered in me, like I'm about to burst and splatter the ground.

I'm not going out for any more drinks lest I inadvertently murder someone.

Yours in love and rage,

Pamela aka Papa Robinson

X

## Re: Anger

FROM: Chris Woods
TO: Pamela Robinson

Hi Pamela, fine by me you're getting angry. In my book, angry women are better than wallowing ones. Anger's more energising, more productive. Look what it's doing for Patricia.

I made two trips to the Greek consulate in the city. I'm registering for Greek citizenship because we don't know how long we are going to be away. I can apply later for a Greek passport if I want. Do I want to? You tell me.

I'm still lying low. Staying right away from Patricia. Keeping away from the twins. God forbid there should be another complaint against me. Lucky I'm leaving town. Take care, Chris

## The opposite to homesickness

FROM: Pamela Robinson
TO: Chris Woods

Hi Chris,

I wish I could leave town. I've spent my life running away—it's my default position. I never stopped to think what I was running from—I only knew if I stopped I'd be devoured. I'm about to find out what happens to a person who can no longer run. Was it me who said Chris was discontented no matter where he was, and that wherever he was it was always the wrong place? Did I say he was the one searching for the faultless home where he might find his happiness? The truth is, I'm beginning to understand I joined my sorrowful longing to his—my *fernweh* to his *fernweh*. There's no word in English for the German word *fernweh*—its closest translation is 'farsickness'—the opposite to homesickness, *heimweh*. *Fernweh* is a longing to be somewhere else—anywhere other than home.

Don't think I'm blind to the distasteful equation of Muaz and Zahiya and Rima and their *heimweh*—unable to return to their home—and me with my *fernweh*, eternally running away from one. There are no sacred scales to weigh the visible ordeal of Muaz and Zahiya and Rima, longing for home, against the hidden ordeal of my brother, longing for anywhere but home, searching for an elsewhere so far away it resembles oblivion. I'm starting to see Scotty longed for elsewhere too—but a permanent elsewhere where no-one would find him.

'Are you ready to begin?' Tünde asks. 'Are you willing to start talking about why you're here?'

I don't tell her about a dream I had of finding my brother dead, hauling Scotty off the dirty carpet, hoisting him onto my shoulder with superhuman strength. I wrapped his cold body in a shroud and cradled him in my arms, keening. Then the shroud was off—he was lying against my bare skin—his skin against mine—and my heartbeat—my desperate longing—returned him to life. When I looked down, Scotty was newly born—except he was also Raphael, bloody against my breast in the delivery room. I held my fresh son who was also my brother, delivered of pain. Oh, dear God—to see Scotty alive again, fresh with chances. To see Raf, unbroken.

Love,
Pamela

## Re: The opposite to homesickness

FROM: Chris Woods

TO: Pamela Robinson

Hi Pamela, I guess I'm more a *heimweh* type of person. There's a big difference between you and me, Pamela. I don't believe in earthly answers, home or elsewhere. Earthly answers are imperfect. Have you talked to your son about beating you up yet?

First big snowfalls of the season here. I've already landed flat on my face. Mike didn't get to finish raking leaves. He won't get to them now till he starts spring yard work.

Mindy's exercise these days is being let out the back door into the garden. She pees a steaming yellow hole in the snow, does her business, then traipses back inside wearing snow boots. Mike or I get so guilty one of us volunteers to walk her around the block. If it's me, I go in the other direction to Patricia's house. She might take a pop at me through a window.

Today it's my turn to take her. Mindy's trembling with excitement because it's her lucky day. She's straining at the lead, pulling my arm off before I'm out the door. I'm bundled up in my fleece knit cap and ear bands, gloves and coat. My scarf is wrapped tight around my face. Only my eyes are exposed. Outside, the water in my eyes freezes over, icicles form on my eyelashes. I'm thinking, *How the hell do I keep living in this godforsaken place?*

Then I congratulate myself on moving to Greece, before I remember I'm going to the coldest part of the country. I'm muttering to myself about how I can never get away from the cold, when *splat,* over I go. Flat on my back, my head bobbing like a beach ball on the ice. I see stars like in a cartoon.

The thing that saves me from splitting my head open are my fleece cap and ear bands. They give my head a double layer of protection. I'm lying there, wondering how I'm going to get upright. Mindy's not acting like a brave dog in a movie. She doesn't try to pull me up by the sleeve. She's sniffing me instead, whining.

Linda from the top of the street appears in front of my face. 'Dear Lord! Are you all right?'

I ask her to help me up. She tries, then falls over too. Me and my neighbour, flat out on the ice, Mindy beside us, trembling. Can my life get any worse? A crazy woman defaming me, my mother dragging me to the other side of the world, two kids hating my guts, and their mom scared out of her wits because of me. Take care, Chris

## Rescue

FROM: Pamela Robinson
TO: Chris Woods

# How did you get up?

## Re: Rescue

FROM: Chris Woods
TO: Pamela Robinson

Hi Pamela, a snowplough happened to be passing. The driver didn't scoop us up in the bucket of his plough. He got out of the driver's seat and picked us up in his arms like we were tiny children. He was the biggest, blackest, kindest snowplough driver in Schenectady, with the biggest hands I've seen in my life.

Still snowing. It's a record for November and we are only halfway through. Mike's been over to Patricia's to throw salt down and clear her drive with the snow blower. She was rabbiting in his ear about Karl, her own son, not coming around to help his widowed mother.

'Is she still trying to sue him?' I asked.

Mike said he didn't know.

Mike has as much interest in other people's lives as he does in the mysterious disappearing clothes I donate to charity. If everyone was like Mike, no-one would know anything about anyone. He's got one friend, Tom Steiner. They went to high school together. Every now and then the boys go out for a drink. I happened to be passing by once, glanced in the window. They were sitting side by side at the bar. Not talking.

'Did Patricia say anything about me? About the letters?'

He shook his head. Men, huh?

I've spent so much time at Mom's, I forgot to think about my own problems. I forgot to think about my own debris. I don't know what a person is supposed to pack for a ghost house when they don't know how long they'll be away. Take care, Chris

247

## Still falling

FROM: Pamela Robinson
TO: Chris Woods

Hi Chris,

Well, I wished I was anywhere other than my own house when Nick turned up this afternoon. Luckily Deb was here—I was cowering in the bedroom.

'You'd better come out,' she said. 'Tell him to his face how things stand.'

I scuttled out the front door, saying over my shoulder as I went out that I was popping out for a minute.

'How long is your pass out?' Nick said. *Ha, ha, ha.*

'You can't keep turning up like this,' I said. 'You know how volatile my situation is.'

'I know,' he said. 'I'm offering to help hose it down.'

We walked around the corner and up around the block, passing the Fake Grass House. 'Wowsers,' he said. 'Fake grass.'

'Yep. No mowing. A lifetime pass.'

'What kind of person has fake grass?' he said.

For the first time in ages, I laughed. I mean, *really* laughed.

'What's so funny?' he said.

I could only shake my head. 'I don't know,' I said. 'It's just funny.'

We soon came to the frangipani tree; the single flower pinned to the sky has disappeared. So many living people passing beneath its vanishing, unwatched beauty and—like everything embodied, once visible—now returned to the watchful mercy of the stars. The flower has gone—I forgot to look and it's disappeared, with or without the guardianship

of my eyes. So many vanishings, heedless of how zealously
we stand guard.

Love,
Pamela
X

## Re: Still falling

FROM: Chris Woods
TO: Pamela Robinson

Hi Pamela, we'll be gone in an instant, honey. Only God remains. Your boyfriend's pretty persistent though, considering he's not getting any cookies from the jar.

The evil twin's persistent, too. She marches into work and, looking stern, she says, 'Mrs Woods, I must speak to you.'

'Excuse me,' I say to my colleagues, who are riveted. I feel like I am being escorted to the headmaster's office.

Muaz walks fast ahead of me down the corridor. I'm puffing after her. 'Muaz! Wait up!'

She stops, but without turning around. When I reach her, she does not turn her head.

'Listen, I'm sorry,' I say. 'I'm really sorry. I made a mistake.'

'Sorry is not enough,' she says, still refusing to look at me.

'Where are we going?'

'Outside,' she says.

'It's freezing out there,' I say.

'Good,' she says.

She keeps walking. At least she's slowed down. Outside in the quadrangle, she leads me to a bench covered in snow. She starts brushing it off with her gloved hand.

'We'll get wet,' I say.

'I don't care,' she says, sitting down.

'This is where I fell over last winter,' I say, pointing. 'Right there.'

'Mrs Woods, why did you do it?' She turns to look at me then. Her eyes are very dark, as black as Kalamata olives. They shine with life, with something I call vigour.

I swallow. 'I had this idea your mom needed to be shocked out of her stupor.'

She keeps looking hard at me. 'Did you not see the grief of her heart? The wound there?'

'Of course I did! That's exactly why I did what I did,' I say. 'Your mom needs to get out of bed, Muaz. You need your mom standing.'

I see she is struggling. Her face is readable as weather. The clouds coming in, something dangerous moving in from the horizon.

'Muaz, honey. I would never do anything to hurt her. Or you.' I take a risk and move my bare hand over her gloved one. 'I'm also freezing out here.'

'She is so sad,' Muaz says, beginning to cry. 'Mrs Woods, she is so sad. We left our home. It is the centre of our hearts.'

She cries harder, leaning into me. Snow starts to fall. I picture us, frozen, covered in snow, human statues cast in mourning pose. Lord, what have I done? Take care, Chris

## Humanity's chorus

FROM: Pamela Robinson
TO: Chris Woods

Oh, Chris—poor Muaz and, my God, poor, grieving Rima. What a picture of grief—the two of you on that cold bench, and Rima stranded in her bed. But look—the truth might not be as ruinous as it first appears. Of course Rima's loss at the centre of her heart is genuine and alive—I don't mean to say her loss is not real and demonstrable. But Tünde suggests the only truth we can ultimately claim is sovereignty over our own hearts—everything else is just supposition. I mean, obviously Rima has lost her home, and she and Muaz and Zahiya are in mourning for everything they have lost—I don't mean to say their losses are not sorely evident. I'm saying something else—something about the dimensions of grief—about how we bear our losses. I'm hopeless at it myself—and I have free lungs and a sky without bombs—but I'm also coming to understand that, like everyone, I'm custodian over a sovereign heart. In the end, who but Rima knows her heart's workings?

You should see the collective hearts every day at the library— humanity's chorus, lining up outside waiting for us to open up every morning. No matter where I've worked—London, Detroit, Sydney—a library is a place of refuge, a modern church: life's thronging congregation, writ small.

Mr Moore comes every Thursday. His wife has dementia— she's in a nursing home—and every week he comes in to pick a new book to read to her. 'We don't know what she hears,' he said this morning. 'She might be listening to every word for all we know.' He brought her in once—she was bent over double and could barely walk—she had forgotten the work of standing upright. She did not know where she was—or even who she was—but Mr Moore led her straight to the counter to introduce me. 'Pamela, this is my wife,' he said. 'Her name is Dot.'

Chris, don't despair—only Rima and her God know the struggle to stand.

With love,

Pamela

X

## Evil eye

FROM: Chris Woods
TO: Pamela Robinson

Hi Plato, what a turn-up for the books: Plato advising Socrates on despair. I thought it was my job to tell you how to breathe. As it happens, I'm avoiding breathless women. I haven't been back to see Rima. Muaz won't talk to me. I heard from Zahiya her mom is still in bed. I'm kicking myself about being so stupid. If Rima's sovereign heart is anything like mine, it's not full of regret.

Muaz and Patricia are not the only ones who won't talk to me. Now Mom's not talking to me. She's giving me the evil eye instead. Only God knows what I did wrong. Mom gives Dora the evil eye and Dora doesn't even notice. I can't tell you why two sisters who grew up in the same house with the same mother have such different relationships to the same mother with the same evil eye.

My own eyes are watching money fly out the window. Shelling out for visas, Mom's medication that she won't be able to get in Greece. Shipping fees for Mom's debris. We still need to pay for new luggage, airline tickets, removal costs. I haven't told Mr Bedford I'm leaving yet. Whatever comes you can be sure humanity's chorus will keep singing that same old tune about bills, bills, bills. Take care, Socrates

## Some happy news

FROM: Pamela Robinson
TO: Chris Woods

Hi Socrates,

Money flying out the window here too—straight into Tünde's pocket. But some good news! Baps bed-wetting device has worked. How narrow is my compass that my life's happiness is measured by my eight-year-old son no longer wetting the bed and—better still—Baps no longer wetting *my* bed. He's back in the sleep-out—master of his own premises, captain of his ship. I won't say I miss his warm breath, his creamy, unwalked feet—but Baps is in his own body and I am back in mine.

But the biggest piece of good news from my small compass is a conversation I had with Raf. I've seen him twice now and the second time I saw him we talked about our fight. We were in the car, not facing each other, so I'm not sure how high that rates on the intimacy scale of conversations. Personally, some of the most intimate conversations of my life have taken place in cars, when I never have to look the other person in the eye.

'I don't know how it happened,' Raf suddenly announced.

I knew what he was talking about but I pretended I didn't. 'How what happened?' I said, my eyes on the road. I was driving him home to Marion's from a rugby match on the other side of the city—unlike Claude, Raf prefers rugby to soccer.

'Oh, nothing,' he said.

'Nothing comes of nothing,' I said. 'Speak up, love.'

'I don't know why I hit you,' he said softly, under his breath.

'I can't hear you, Raf. What did you say?' Of course I heard him—I heard the powerful struggle to heave the words to his mouth.

'I don't know why I hit you, Mum,' he said. 'I'm sorry. It won't happen again.'

I risked a glance at him—he was looking out the window.

'How do you know it won't?'

'I just know,' he said.

I didn't immediately respond. I was thinking of all the things I could say—about how life is one long endless lesson in loss and renewal—one ceaseless cycle of birth and decay and rebirth again—one giant process of fuck-ups and fresh dawns.

'I miss Dad,' he said, and I heard him with both my ears and heart then—the knife of loss—everything in this life he will never see the likes of again.

'I know, Raf. I know,' I said, reaching for his hand. He took my hand—holding it as if he were a small child—and we held each other's hands until I took mine back to concentrate on steering.

Much love,

Plato

X

## Out of bed

FROM: Chris Woods
TO: Pamela Robinson

Hi Pamela, wow, you finally had the conversation. I'm happy for your happiness. Sounds like you might be turning off that circular track to drive down a different road. We've got a little good news round these parts too: Rima's out of bed. I just went to see her.

I took a bunch of peace-making gifts. A bottle of Greek honey for Rima, a pair of red leather gloves for Muaz, an embroidered velvet scarf for Zahiya.

I'm knocking on the door. The snow's falling. I'm hoping they're going to open the door, not leave me standing in the snow like some orphan out of Dickens.

Zahiya opens the door.

'Hi, honey. You going to ask me in?'

She turns around to look behind her. Is Muaz standing there, shaking her head, telling her no?

Zahiya lets me in. I stamp the snow off my boots, taking them off by the door.

Across the other side of the room Muaz and her mother are standing side by side. Rima is out of bed. It's the first thing I notice.

'I have gifts,' I say. 'I've come to apologise.'

Rima rushes across the room, takes both my hands in hers. I put down the bag I'm carrying. She's speaking fast in Arabic.

'She wants to thank you,' says Zahiya. 'She wants to thank you for everything you have done.'

I look at Muaz, who hasn't moved an inch. 'I don't want to thank you,' she says. 'I want you to leave this house.'

Zahiya puts a hand on my arm. 'I'm sorry, Mrs Woods. My sister is very angry.'

Rima is still holding my hands. 'She asks if you want tea,' says Zahiya.

'Please leave,' says Muaz.

Zahiya starts speaking to Muaz in Arabic. Rima starts speaking to them both. Everyone is arguing.

'OK, OK,' I say. 'I made a mistake. I apologise from the bottom of my heart.'

I pick up the bag I brought. 'I just wanted to give you these.' I give Rima her gift, and Zahiya.

I walk over to Muaz with her gift. She takes it and flings it to the ground. Rima is shouting, Zahiya starts crying, Muaz stalks out of the room.

'I guess I'd better go,' I say.

Zahiya nods, still crying.

I trudge through the snow to the bus stop (our car is in for repairs: more money flying out the window). I'm thinking: *I was only trying to help*. Take care, Chris

### Re: Out of bed

FROM: Pamela Robinson
TO: Chris Woods

Hi Chris,

Why don't you concentrate on helping yourself for a change? Stay home and sort through your junk—decide what you're going to pack for your new life. That's really wonderful news about Rima getting out of bed—and bravo you for being brave enough to try your high-risk shock treatment. Now all you need is an experimental mental health care plan for Patricia. But seriously, Chris, my advice is to forget Patricia—forget about helping everyone else for now—and concentrate on YOU.

Much love,

Pamela

X

## Re: Re: Out of bed

FROM: Chris Woods
TO: Pamela Robinson


Who do you think you are? My mother? I can get free advice any time from Mrs Calliope Pappas over at St Sophia's. She doesn't charge me $150 bucks an hour either. Concentrate on your own problems, Plato.

## Er . . . sorry

FROM: Pamela Robinson
TO: Chris Woods

Hi Socrates,

OK, knuckles duly rapped—again. I'm one of those annoying people who needs to learn their lesson not once—not three times—but many times over. I'm paying Tunde $150 an hour to be taught my over-anxious thinking might be a form of avoidance—and all the while here's me believing if I thought about my problems hard enough I'd eventually come to a solution.

'I wonder how you see contemplation,' she said yesterday. 'If, for you, contemplation might be a form of resistance. Do you think we become what we contemplate? That contemplation leads to behaviour?'

She knows anxiety grips me by the throat—my ceaseless worries and fears for my sons—but she also knows I'm beginning to understand its role in keeping me locked in my house of suffering. In the choice between staying inside or going out into the unforgiving light, I seem to have chosen darkness and resistance.

Yours in dismay,
Plato
X

## Change

FROM: Chris Woods
TO: Pamela Robinson

Hi Pamela, looks like I'm going out into the light, whether I like it or not. I've resigned. The big surprise is I'm eligible for a redundancy payout. We've booked our tickets. Mom's moving out of St Sophia's and in with us the week before Christmas. We fly out 12 January. Take care, Chris

## Happy birthday to me ☺

FROM: Pamela Robinson
TO: Chris Woods

Hi Chris,

You're really going—flying away—stepping off the map! I can't help feeling your new life is going to be fantastic—I don't know why—I just sense you've been stuck on the same old track—like me, except in a different way. I'm losing my devotion to flying away; it's falling from me, and a yearning to stay rooted to the spot is growing instead. Nothing separates me from my desire to create a new map of home. I'm getting closer to something—I'm beginning to understand my task is to stand fast and meet my losses. I'm fifty-two tomorrow and I feel like I'm about to learn where the angels fly. I feel like I'm just getting started.

With love,
Pamela
X

## Dialogue on Meeting Loss and Happy birthday

FROM: Chris Woods
TO: Pamela Robinson

Dear Plato,

1. We meet our losses however we can.

2. Happy birthday to you. Appropriate emojis etcetera.

Take care, Socrates

## CHRIS!!!

FROM: Pamela Robinson
TO: Chris Woods

Hi again,

Thanks for the birthday wishes—and, goodness, what a birthday it was. I'VE SPOKEN TO CHRIS!! I can't believe it!! Let me tell you what happened—we were having a celebratory dinner at the flat—Prisha, Deb, her brother Paul—and Raphael. It's the first time the boys have been together for dinner at home since Raf moved out. Baps was beside himself with joy about Raf being here—rushing around trying to get Souris to perform tricks for Raf—showing Raf where Souris sleeps on his bed—showing off the map of the world I let him pin to the wall. Claude was happy too—although trying his best not to show it. I made the boys' favourite dessert—Jacqueline's chocolate mousse with dark chocolate and egg whites—and, in the middle of it all, I SPOKE TO CHRIS! Baps had the phone up to my ear before I realised who was on the other end—the phone squeezed between my shoulder and the side of my face—my hands full—I was in the middle of taking rice off the stove, transferring a boiling saucepan to the sink—and when I heard Chris's voice I almost dropped the pan.

'Sorry, Pamela,' he said. 'I didn't intend for Baptiste to pass the phone to you.' I put the pan in the sink—the air left my chest—I felt my knees crumple.

'Hello?' he said. 'Are you there?'

Baps was standing beside me, grinning—Souris around his neck like a fur.

'Pamela?' Chris said again. 'Well, since I'm here I may as well wish you happy birthday. *Joyeux anniversaire de Paris.*'

'Thank you,' I said. I didn't know what to say next.

Chris said nothing either.

Then Baps was gone—the phone too—Chris's voice—all our words. Why are the truest words the ones nobody said?

Much love,

Pamela

X

## Words

FROM: Chris Woods
TO: Pamela Robinson

Hi Pamela, well, what do you know? A voice through cloud. What did I say about silence being a form of speech? Sounds to me like you two are laying down the first tracks into open space. Congratulations.

Around here, it's better to have no words. Since Mom arrived, Mike's had a personality transplant. I have to watch what words I say around him, as well as the words I say around Mom. I'm holed up in our bedroom, writing this on my phone. Mike's in the kitchen helping Mom with dinner.

This afternoon I ask her about a guy who used to live in our village.

'Who is this guy?' she asks.

'I can't remember his name,' I say. 'That's why I'm asking. A little guy. Not much taller than me. I think his mother had only one hand.'

'For what reason do you ask about this little guy?'

I shrug. 'Oh, forget it. It's nothing.'

Mike butts in. I thought he was downstairs in the basement. 'Yeah, for what reason do you ask about this little guy whose mother had only one hand?'

'Nothing. Apropos of nothing,' I say.

Mike snorts. 'As any fool knows, nothing is apropos of nothing.'

I nearly fall over. Mike *never* speaks like this. Mike wouldn't know an apropos if he fell over one.

'What's it to you all of a sudden?' I say.

He looks at me strangely. 'I'm interested to hear why my wife is asking about some guy in Greece. My wife who's going to Greece without her husband.'

It's my turn to look at him strangely. 'But you didn't want to come, Mike! I asked you. You said no.'

Mom's at the kitchen table, her coffee cup paused, enjoying the show. 'What are you looking at?' I say to her. 'Mind your own business. Butt out.'

'What word did I say?' she says. 'I did not hear myself speak yet.'

'Thank the Lord for small mercies,' I say. 'I've had it with you two. I'm taking Mindy for a walk.'

I don't fall over this time. I see Patricia in the distance. I'm kind of disappointed when her car turns out of her driveway and heads up the road because I am wearing my fury tie. I feel like socking her in the mouth. Take care, Chris

## All change

FROM: Pamela Robinson
TO: Chris Woods

Hi Chris,

Whoa—all change at your place! Mike sounds as if he's heaving words up from his heart—which can only be a good thing, surely? No more news of Rima and the girls? All change here, too—albeit in a more minor key. The boys finished school yesterday. Christmas up ahead—our second as our newly reconstituted family—then the long summer break. Raf heads off to Queensland next month on holiday with his other, 'better' family. Marion and I have had tentative discussions about him moving back home in the new year. Raf and I haven't discussed the subject directly.

Nick and I caught up for a Christmas drink this week. He's a sweet man, funny and kind—he's probably exactly the sort of man I should have chosen for a husband. He seems so uncomplicated—so frank and open—clear as a sunny day—not clouded and inscrutable as Chris appeared to me, a dark lake whose bottom I could not see. I wanted enigmatic—not light and untroubled. I craved Chris's alluring air of misery and depth. How long it's taken me to understand what everyone else instinctively knows—how to join your happiness to someone else's happiness, instead of yoking two miseries together. All week I've been hearing Chris's deep and—still!—beguiling voice in my head.

I told Tünde about having a drink with Nick, about going to the cemetery with him. Her advice is not to take any further walks with cemetery-loving Englishmen—but if I *do* go on further walks, I should be careful not to let the boys know. Tünde is not impressed with the whole idea of Nick. 'Do you think you've got room for any more emotional engagement in your life?' she asked.

Does she think I don't know the answer?

Much love,

Pamela

X

## Happy Christmas

FROM: Chris Woods
TO: Pamela Robinson

Hi Pamela, I hope you *do* know the answer. To be honest, it's not entirely clear to me that you do. You're not swimming in open water yet, honey.

Over here in Schenectady we're still up to our butts in snow, counting down to the Feast of the Epiphany. We don't have a fireplace so we can't keep the *καλλικάντζαρος* away. Mom's rigged up an emergency bowl of holy water and a sprig of basil. She's dipping her cross in the water and sprinkling it around the house like she's archbishop of Athens.

Every other culture has elves, Santa's happy helpers giving out gifts. Greeks have *καλλικάντζαρος*, evil sprites who live underground except for the twelve days of Christmas. They return to the surface every Christmas to wreak havoc and annoy the crap out of everyone. Dora and I could barely sleep Christmas Eve, not because we were excited about presents in the morning, but because of our terror of hairy elves sawing off our noses in the night.

Wishing you and your sons a happy *καλλικάντζαρος*-free Christmas. God bless, Chris

## Happy Christmas to you!

FROM: Pamela Robinson
TO: Chris Woods

Hi Chris,

Happy Christmas to you, too—here in summery Ashfield an evil sprite-free day was had by all: lunch around the table—us four—north, south, east and west—our new small planet. A dish of turkey for Souris—and then the greatest of unexpected gifts.

After lunch I dropped Raphael home, but when I stopped outside Marion's house he didn't jump straight out of the car without a backward glance like he usually does. He got out and walked slowly around to my side—my window was down—popped his head in and kissed me on the cheek. Then he stood and looked me clean in the eye.

'*Merci*, Maman,' he said. 'Thanks for everything.'

He wasn't thanking me for Christmas lunch.

Much love,

Pamela

X

## Farewells

FROM: Chris Woods
TO: Pamela Robinson

Hi Pamela, now that's what I call progress. Your kid sounds like he's thought things through. Thinking's all well and good but it doesn't necessarily take you anywhere you want to go. I guess Raphael's trying a different kind of thinking to the anxious over-thinking favoured by his mom.

So, work had a farewell party for me. It was kind of weird. A lot of people are away on vacation. They booked a room at this place which turned out to be a rodeo bar. Mr Bedford and Letitia and Becky. (No Tracey, she's in Florida with her husband.) A few girls from admin, from finance, from procurement. I'd rather crawl in a hole than find myself in the centre of a room being presented with a book token for $200 by Mr Bedford.

'Is there anyone here who *doesn't* know Mrs Woods?' he says. 'Who hasn't benefited from a kind note or a comforting chat from her when you're down? I'm betting most of you have had at least one phone call from her.'

I keep my eyes on the floor. I hear Letitia's voice. 'Like maybe a million,' she says.

Everyone laughs. I'm thinking: *Whose idea was it to have this damn thing*? If it was Letitia's, remind me to kill her.

The rodeo bar has a mechanical bull. A mechanical bull in a padded pit, so you don't sue when you fall off (though they still make you sign a release form). It was Letitia's idea.

I told you about Letitia? First black female New York State 400-metre hurdles champion? She's six foot, thin as a rail, and wears one of those counter things on her wrist so she knows how many circles she's running around in. She runs marathons. She doesn't drink alcohol, coffee, anything with sugar. At work, she brings in green juices for lunch. Naturally she's first on the mechanical bull. Everyone else needs tequila shots before they can even think of climbing on.

I'm watching everyone making fools of themselves. I'm watching people urge Mr Bedford to take a ride. I'm thinking: *Do these folk even know me*? I guess they do—they bought me a voucher from Barnes and Noble. Do they think the same person who appreciates a Barnes and Noble voucher is going to appreciate a mechanical bull?

You can sit in a room with someone for thirty years and not know the first thing about them. All those years, ice on the road, falling leaves, summer arriving. We sat in the same room breathing the same air, babies were born, people died. I'm standing there and it's like I'm in a movie. I'm looking around, everything's real clear, but it's like the sound's turned off. Suddenly I can't stand it another second. I run away from my own farewell party.

In the car I cry all the way home. Maybe I expected too much. Maybe I thought I was in some book where we we'd meet for cocktails at the Carlyle. Maybe I thought I was someone else. Take care, Chris

## Re: Farewells

FROM: Pamela Robinson
TO: Chris Woods

Oh, sweetheart—you're you—the one and only. You're Socrates who teaches sad girls to ride bikes and mothers how to stand. You're the Kind Gal who rings an invisible woman on the other side of the planet in her darkest hour, who shoots forth a flare of light into compassionless space. Chris, you teach words everyone knows but forgot—you wrote that book in which love is death's answer. That's the book you're in—that bright book of life—please be no-one else—ever—but yourself.

With love,

Plato

X

## Thanks

FROM: Chris Woods
TO: Pamela Robinson

Hi Plato, thank you for your words. I didn't realise I wrote a book. Maybe I can order it for Mom to read on the plane. Did I tell you I went to high school with someone who lost her daughter on Flight 800 which exploded off Long Island? To be honest, I'm not looking forward to flying. Take care, Socrates

## Courage

FROM: Pamela Robinson
TO: Chris Woods

Hi Chris,

I love flying—it's easier to see the magnitude of existence from above the earth—to sense the movement of time—the span of a human life. Those hours inside a frail skin of aluminium remind me how briefly we flicker, how short our reign among the perishing many. Two hundred human souls aloft in the sky, each soul doggedly itself.

A woman I know just hanged herself. We lived together in the nineties in a shared student house in Glebe. The thing I remember best about Carol is that once she borrowed a favourite dress of mine and returned it with the zip broken. She was a big girl—too big for the dress—yet she squeezed herself in. She wore the dress to a gig at the Phoenician Club and came home with the drummer.

In my head I have this picture of her sitting in the sun at the kitchen table the next morning, rolling a smoke. She was still wearing the dress—the drummer was asleep upstairs—and the zip was broken. She was a happy girl on a sunny morning in Glebe in 1991, wearing a dress with a broken zip—one moment out of all time. Surely it's our task to live this moment—to live every moment—even if it means believing yourself already dead before you summon the courage to open the front door? Surely we must live as if we don't hear the gunfire—as if planes don't fall from the sky? Carol lost her courage—as I so nearly lost mine—and if I could I would rush back to that vanished Glebe morning. I would gather her up and let her stay in that sunny moment. But I can't—I can't—I can't hold up my hand to stop time and return. All I can do is learn to walk forwards into all my coming moments, lit or shrouded. I'm learning how to mourn—how to marry the wounded facts to the necessary world without screaming. I have to leave those already gone to their own mislaid fates—leave the past in order to meet the future. I'm so happy, Chris, that you are meeting yours.

With much love,
Pamela
X

## Re: Courage

FROM: Chris Woods
TO: Pamela Robinson

Hi Pamela, I'm sorry about your friend. Like I said, we meet our losses, and our futures, in our own ways. Here's me trying to forget planes don't fall from the sky by calmly packing my clothes: four sweaters, two coats, twelve tubes of Crest (I hate Greek toothpaste, I just remembered) and six pairs of shoes. I'm meeting my future while figuring out if I've got enough space in my luggage to fit a dozen boxes of Honey Nut Cheerios if I take them out of their packaging. Greeks travel with pigs, goats, chickens. What's a few boxes of Cheerios among friends? Take care, Chris

## Going away

FROM: Pamela Robinson
TO: Chris Woods

Hi Chris,

I'm packing too—no Cheerios. We're flying to Queensland tomorrow —it's nearly midnight and I'm nowhere near finished packing. We've got a whole two weeks at the beach—not quite the same as flying to Greece, but I'm happy. I managed to find a house to rent for less than a million dollars—it's the last two weeks of the school holidays so I was lucky to find anything— and I lucked out twice by getting one of the last remaining old beach houses at Coolum, with the emphasis on shabby *sans* chic. It's close enough to Noosa, too, for Raf to visit—Deb's staying here to water the plants and feed Souris. I'm looking forward to unravelling myself in the heat—to a lumpy bed in a fibro shack—to eating peanut butter straight from the jar.

Look at you, Chrisanthi Xenia, flying away! Leaving so soon—you must be beside yourself with excitement.

Sending much love,

Pamela

X

## Leaving

FROM: Chris Woods
TO: Pamela Robinson

Hi Pamela, not so much excitement as a sick, sorrowing feeling. The same old sadness worming its way out again. Mike's taken Mom to buy flight socks. I'm sitting alone with my sorrow in an empty living room, writing to you, looking at my house which I'm leaving. I love its coloured walls. I love the dresser Mike built when we were first married, tucked against the green of the living room wall he painted. You can tell a lot about a person from her house.

I'm looking at Boris curled in my lap, which reminds me of Kathleen. I'm looking at Mindy, trembling at my feet, which reminds me of the day Mike brought her home. It was a snowy afternoon like this. I thought I was going to die of pain. I was home from hospital with no baby. Not everyone who gives birth becomes a mother, Pamela.

Mike had cleaned out the baby's room. He brought a puppy out of the kitchen. We didn't know Mindy's trembling was something she would never grow out of. She was so small she couldn't get up the stairs by herself. She was a living creature I had to care for or she would die.

Mike was so handsome when he was young. I was so proud he wanted to go out with me. I married him not knowing marriage was for life. Mike has loved me so hard, and for so long.

What have I done in this world but trace my small corner of the earth? I have mapped my here to there, known my few. Kathleen with her colour-coded clothes. Patricia and Gene who wasted their days fighting an inside war. Rima and Muaz and Zahiya. Mike. I never forgot the sight of Lorraine walking away from her daughter.

Only once in my life have I left the map of Schenectady. I feel like a long-ago explorer setting sail, not knowing where the world ends. I'm not brave like you, Pamela. Take care, Chris

## Re: Leaving

FROM: Pamela Robinson
TO: Chris Woods


Chris, Chris—I didn't know—I'm in tears—and so sorry for my assumptions—for trampling over your pain in the midst of mine—for everything I did not see. Can I call you? What's a good time? Oh, Chris, I'm not brave—running away is not an act of bravery—it's an unwillingness to sit still long enough to enter the archive of your griefs. If everyone was like me there'd be no houses with coloured walls—no people sitting in offices for thirty years breathing the same air. And aren't all of us—home or away—sailing the way those ancient sailors did? Travelling our blind lives by way of the stars ... Please can I phone? I just checked—your number's stored in my phone from that time you called me. It's not too late at night for me to call is it? X

## Re: Re: Leaving

FROM: Chris Woods
TO: Pamela Robinson

Hi Plato, my turn to tell you I'm OK. No need to phone. Silence is a form of speech, remember. I told you keeping some things unsaid is my preference. Maybe not as unsaid as Mike and Tom Steiner, but somewhere in between. We fly out tomorrow. Maybe you and I are swapping lives. Take care, Socrates

## Bon voyage!

FROM: Pamela Robinson
TO: Chris Woods

Welcome out of the cave then, my friend. It's colder out here but the stars are beautiful. X

### Re: Bon Voyage!

FROM: Chris Woods
TO: Pamela Robinson

Hi Pamela, this comes to you from the holding pen, aka transit at London Heathrow. Would my mother fly direct? She would not. The reason? Ay-rabs. That's how Mom says it. 'How can you trust people who hide their faces?' So, no Emirates (direct to Athens) but British Airways, via London, because she likes the Queen. Thirteen hours.

Mom's sitting clamped to a chair, holding tight to her purse, while I'm over here on the internet. She thought London Heathrow would be full of people dressed like Her Majesty. Her eyes are popping out of her head at the black folk and Ay-rabs. It's just like being home in Schenectady.

Did I enjoy the flight? I did not. My travel socks are so tight blood seemed likely to burst from my eyeballs. An hour out I was dying to pee but I was too scared to move from my seat. I kept picturing myself stuck in the john with my pants around my ankles. The stewardess breaking the door down. I didn't sleep a wink. I don't like the idea of people seeing me with my mouth open. Sleep's private. No way am I letting anyone see my face with dreams on it.

I've sent up a lot of prayers for you and your sons, Pamela. Maybe God is finally getting around to answering them. Take care, Chris

## Answers

FROM: Pamela Robinson
TO: Chris Woods

Hi Chris,

I'm glad someone's answering—whether it's God or Allah or the heavens above. Thank you, Chris—I'd love to have your faith, but here I am, down here with my earthly answers. For the moment, I have no questions—only beach and sky—fish and chips—Frisbees on the sand—and my flailing boys learning how to battle the Pacific.

They're not used to the roar and pulse of an Australian ocean—the great muscle of a powerful sea—they're used to the dainty rustle of la Manche. They loved their grandmother's beach at Deauville—the sand fine and smooth, turning spiky as it got closer to the water—shells and rocks and grit, sharp as sticks. The sea there is tidal, arterial—arctic currents flowing down from the North Sea—rushing in fast only at high tide. The boys adored it, even on cold days when the sea was so far away—brackish, dull, like river water running all the way to England.

How Scotty would have laughed at them today—my frail boys pitted against the mighty Pacific—that ocean he lived in like his own skin. We grew up on the northern beaches of Sydney—our lives were surfboards and wax and salt on our eyelashes. We learned the ocean young. Compared to my boys, I feel like a warrior when I stride out into the slap of it. Like Scotty I can read the ocean—I see rips and sandbanks and unseen dangers—I never need a lifesaver's flag to tell me where to swim.

At last—something about me to impress my sons! Their mother is a dolphin—their mother is strong and fleet and capable of fighting any wave—faster than a speeding bullet—able to leap tall buildings in a single bound—more powerful than a locomotive! You should see Claude's face as he sits on a towel watching me emerge from the ocean—you should see Raf flailing in the shallows, watching in awe as his mother swims out the back—beyond the break—out into the wild, freeing sea.

With love,

Pamela

X

## My beloved homeland

FROM: Chris Woods
TO: Pamela Robinson

Hi Pamela, hell, even I'm impressed. I couldn't catch a wave if my life depended on it.

Mom hasn't stopped since we landed. She was second off the plane because she sweet-talked the stewardess into letting her down the front. She disappeared down the walkway. She's got a plastic hip, right? She's got some secret determination powering her forwards. 'Excuse me, sorry,' I'm saying, trying to catch up with my eighty-seven-year-old mother. Back at St Sophia's, Mom could barely walk from one room to another.

It's too late to travel to Kalavryta by the time we get into Athens. Does Mom want to crash, like me? She does not. She wants to put her bags down and head straight out. She wants to go down to the lobby and get a map. We're outside within ten minutes of arriving. Turns out our hotel is in the middle of the Plaka.

So, I'm eating dinner at nearly midnight at some over-priced tourist joint. Our table is on the street. I'm watching an endless stream of people organised into distinguishable tribes. Italians are nothing like Swedes. Chinese are nothing like Germans. Greeks are nothing like Americans. Rima at home in Schenectady, drinking boiled grass tea, slats over her eyes. So many ways of being human.

I'm half listening to Mom arguing with some old Greek guy at the next table. This country is supposed to be bankrupt. Greece owes seventy-five zillion dollars to the rest of the world. Tell that to the Greeks drinking and smoking and talking in cafes and bars and restaurants. Outnumbering tourists twenty to one, by my calculations. Do Greeks ever shut up?

They've got opinions on everything. Mom's arguing with the old guy about taxes, government bailouts. About whether Greece went to the dogs after the Colonels, or before. Who knew Mom knew so much about Greek politics? She's arguing with the old Greek guy, with waiters, with the cafe owners.

We just got back from eating breakfast. Mom's downstairs arguing with the waitress. Waitresses in Greece don't know there's supposed to be a separation between people eating at the table and people serving them. She might as well have joined us and chowed in. The waitress has been holding a tray of dirty dishes for twenty minutes, arguing with Mom about Yanis Varoufakis.

Got to shoot. We need to find a travel agent and organise a car. No way am I driving. Mom's paying someone to drive us to Kalavryta. Three hours, as the angels fly. Take care, Chris

PS You know you still can't flush toilet paper down the toilet here? There's a little plastic bin beside the john where you put the toilet paper. Greece has the same sewage system it had when Socrates was a boy.

## Re: My beloved homeland

FROM: Pamela Robinson

TO: Chris Woods

Hi Chris,

Funny about the toilet paper—I remember that from Greece in the nineties. Chris and I took the boys to a cheap accommodation-and-meals resort on Crete. The kids ran wild the whole time with a pack of other boys—Claude said when he grew up he was going to move to Greece and become a ferry boat driver. How happy I would be if that came true—but in truth my happiness lies in Claude being delivered into adulthood in any shape or form—that he not only grows to pass through its gates but continues walking gladly ahead. I don't care what he does—I only want Claude and Raphael and Baptiste to walk into their futures. Oh, Chris, how lucky they are to have one—I keep thinking of your loss—I wish you'd told me earlier.

Raf's still here—between him and Claude I'm being eaten out of house and home. Baps has his small child's pickiness—he doesn't like the fur on fat summer peaches—he doesn't like the gooey stuff inside figs. But Claude and Raf could eat the world—bread, fish, stones—their mouths are empty—their legs. What a joy to see their hunger—what a happy thing to see my boys with appetites which seem indistinguishable from an appetite for the world. They sleep—go to the beach—they eat—everything in them woken up—ravenous. I'm getting hungry too—I want to eat everything, just like I wanted to eat that flowering tree in Jacqueline's spring garden. You should see the delicious Queensland sky, Chris—high and wide and

effortless—beneficent as the dome of heaven—and us, hungry
for life, breathing by the sea beneath it.

    With love,

    Pamela

    X

## Re: Re: My beloved homeland

FROM: Chris Woods
TO: Pamela Robinson

Hi Pamela, You are not going to believe what just happened. I told you we had to find a travel agency to hire a car and driver? We just got back. I'm writing this in the lobby. I can't believe it.

We walked into some random travel agency. The nearest one to the hotel. Everyone's talking Greek, I get maybe half the conversation. Everyone seems a little too overexcited, even for Greeks. The travel agent, who is a million years old, jumps up from his chair, races around from behind the counter, embraces Mom. Everyone starts crying. He's crying, Mom's crying, the girls who work at the other desks are crying. Women from the room at the back come out, shouting, clapping their hands.

'Mom?' I'm saying in the middle of it. 'What's happening?' She's too busy crying and embracing everyone. I'm being hugged by strangers. I'm like a deaf person trying to hear.

Mom suddenly rushes out to the street, leaving her credit card on the counter. 'Mom! Your card!' I say, chasing her out the door. I grab her by the arm.

'I know this is your beloved homeland,' I say, 'but Greece has thieves, just like America. You can't leave your credit card on the counter. What just happened in there?'

She makes that *pffft* sound. Tears catch in the cracks of her face. 'I trust him,' she says.

'You just met him!' I say, maybe a little too loud.

She tells me I don't know what I'm talking about.

'He is the man who put me and Yiayia and Katina on the boat.'

'What boat?'

293

'The boat to America,' she says.

Out of all the travel agencies in Athens, out of all the travel agents in Athens aged ninety and still alive and working, Mom chances upon the very man who sold her the ticket to America.

He's the man who felt so bad for the three country hicks from Kalavryta who lived through the massacre that he put their suitcases in the back of his car and drove them to Piraeus before taking their picture and escorting them to their cabins.

He's the guy who took the photograph of them holding hands before they boarded the ship to the country with gold flowing from the taps.

Does God know we're coming? The driver's here to take us to the ghosts. More later. Take care, Chris

## God's geometry

FROM: Pamela Robinson
TO: Chris Woods

WTF!! How can something like that even happen? I don't believe in fate, as you know—but that's enough to make anyone bow down before heaven. Who doesn't like symmetry—life's chaos rounded up into shape—a pleasing pattern when previously there was none? My goodness—how's that for God's geometry. Maybe God does know you're coming. I suspect He already knows what you're going to find.

Love,

Pamela

X

## What God wants

FROM: Chris Woods
TO: Pamela Robinson

Hi Pamela, here's what God wanted me to find: a toilet that's not working. We know about not putting paper down the bowl. Is it too much to ask when you pull a toilet chain the toilet flushes?

Here's me carrying pans of water from the kitchen to pour down the john. I don't want to think about where it's going. There's a tank for 'dirty water' you pump out when it's full. Whether that includes sewage I do not know. I wish Mike was here to fix the john. At least the internet's working. Take care, Chris

## Re: What God wants

FROM: Pamela Robinson
TO: Chris Woods

Oh, Socrates—the romance of Greek village life. I googled Kalavryta—there are snow chalets for rent! Whenever I think of Greece I picture the sea, or Athens in the heat. What I don't picture is Greeks on skis—frankly, it sounds wrong. What a fine sense of national stereotypes I have—I'm as bad as someone who believes every Australian is a white descendant of a convict, with a koala bear in a tree in her garden.

If you won't send a photograph of yourself, can you at least send one of the ghost house?

Yours in hope,

Plato

X

TUE 21/01 4.56PM

## The ghost house

FROM: Chris Woods

TO: Pamela Robinson

Hi Pamela, the broken shutter gets fixed tomorrow. We can't patch and whitewash till the weather clears in spring. You see that crazy balcony? Mom paid Harry, the guy who's fixing the shutters, 180 euros to repair it. I don't care to stand on it. It feels unsafe. It fits one chair, maybe two. It fits an old lady with binoculars casing the joint.

The Katsoulis family from next door looked after our house. First old Mrs Katsoulis, then her daughter Maria. Now it's Maria's daughter Gregoria. Everyone knows which family belongs to which house. Even the abandoned ones. The Germans burned most of the town. Locked everyone in the schoolhouse, the women and kids, burned it down with everyone in it. Then they torched the rest of the village.

Our house survived. So did Gregoria's next door, and the one next to that. Also a couple more houses further up the hill. Most of the tourists who come have no idea most of the town is new, rebuilt post World War II. The young Greek kids in their shiny cars driving down from Athens, they know. Some visit the new museum dedicated to the massacre. The museum didn't exist last time I was here.

The ghost house is freezing. I've settled Mom on the ground floor, to be near the fire. I'm huddled upstairs, under twenty-five goat-hair blankets. It's like the Princess and the Pea, except I'm the pea. I can't move under the weight of the blankets. Every morning my limbs are stiff from being immobile all night, as well as being snap-frozen.

So, Mom moved five thousand miles so she could watch Greek TV 24/7. Greek TV is circa 1982, women looking like they've stepped out of *Dynasty*. Talk shows using big, old-fashioned microphones, like they've never heard of ear monitors.

The wall in the living room where Mom sleeps has three rescued photographs of old dudes when they were young, off to fight the Ottomans or the Balkans or whoever they were fighting. Mom and Katina were born in this room. Yiayia too, and her mother. My advice is not to move to Greece if you don't care for the past following you around. Everyone knows your business. Past and present. Everyone talks about everyone. I forgot the most common expression in Kalavryta is *Τι θα λεει ο κοσμος?* What will the world say? Like anyone cares. Take care, Chris

## Moving home

FROM: Pamela Robinson

TO: Chris Woods

Hi Chris,

You didn't tell me the ghost house was so beautiful. It's got that neo-classical majesty—I was thinking something more Greek island-style—small, curved and white. It looks big—lucky you're upstairs, away from the chatter of Greek TV. I must say being here without television is wonderful—the boys were horrified this old shack has no TV, no Netflix, no DVDs, no internet. They quickly used up all the data on their phones and I refused to buy more, so Raf spent some of his Christmas money buying some—not only for himself, but for Claude. How's that for brotherly love?

Guess what? Raf wants to move home! He wants to move back before the new school year starts—my heart flew from my chest when he said it. We were on the veranda, watching the sun setting, and it was as if my happiness was recomposing itself in the sky. The sky was aflame—incandescent—my happiness part of it—every thank you I possessed flying to the sun. I couldn't speak—my eyes awash—this time with tears for the bright flame of love.

Yours in happiness,

Pamela

X

## Re: Moving Home

FROM: Chris Woods
TO: Pamela Robinson

Hi Pamela, that is the best news. What a great start to your year. I have some good news too: an email from Zahiya. Muaz is on the team for the New York State Mathematics League championships. Rima is back to bossing Zahiya and Muaz around. Rima's even talking about inviting Brandon over for dinner.

Zahiya finished her email this way: *Mrs Woods we miss you like a dream which left our eyes before we could remember.* Poetry, huh?

No email from Muaz. Like you say, we have to keep walking forwards. Sometimes I just wish everyone could come along. Take care, Chris

**Sorry again!**

FROM: Pamela Robinson
TO: Chris Woods

Hi Chris,

Sorry to go AWOL—it's been frantic here—school starting—new books and bags and shoes to be bought—and RAPHAEL IS HOME.

How can I tell you what it was like—knowing your story? You never got to bring your baby home. I don't want to upset you—I'll just say that seeing Raf walk in the front door was one of the happiest moments of my life.

Sending much love,

Pamela

X

## Village life

FROM: Chris Woods
TO: Pamela Robinson

Hi Pamela, look, I lost my daughter a long time ago. My sorrows are under God's hand. Sometimes I don't even mind my sadness because without it I wouldn't know how big my love was.

Mom's had her first fight. She got out her fury tie for an argument she's having with another old lady. Mom says the other old lady is spreading rumours about her and has the evil eye. What one old lady says about another old lady I do not know. It only proves to me old ladies are girls on the inside. Take care, Chris

## Re: Village life

FROM: Pamela Robinson
TO: Chris Woods

Hi Chris,

I'm glad I didn't upset you by telling you about Raphael. I'm humbled by the way you live your life, the way you seem to instinctively know everyone's sorrows and joys—like Tünde but without the qualifications! I'm back under her careful tutelage—feeling less violent—more willing to move closer to some original sadness. I'm addressing my ghosts—and not dying of remembering.

Baps turned nine today. He seems so much older than he was this time last year—he was so anxious then, so clingy—a frightened baby boy. Now he's not only grown a couple of inches—I had to buy new school trousers—he's grown into his own self. He's still funny—chopsticks up his nostrils is still his favourite trick in Japanese restaurants. He still adores playing with Souris. But he's growing up and away—shrugging me off at the school gate—swatting me away if Raf or Claude catch me cuddling him.

He asked for an old-fashioned globe of the world light for his birthday. It's by the table beside his bed—when I went in to kiss him goodnight he was spinning it gently. 'Papa is there,' he said, tracing a line, 'and I am here. Soon he arrives here for his holiday.'

My heart lurched. 'Yes,' I said. 'Papa is coming for a holiday. Where will you go?'

'To the beach,' he said. 'I told him Australia has big waves which Maman surfs.'

I smiled. 'I hope Dad likes big waves.'

'I will teach him how to surf them,' he said.

'Excellent. *Joyeux anniversaire, chéri.* I love you, Baps.'

'Love ya, Mum,' he said, rolling over.

Yikes. Without me noticing Baptiste has turned into an Australian. Tell me what it's like turning into a Greek.

Love ya,

Pamela

XXXX

## Turning into a Greek

FROM: Chris Woods
TO: Pamela Robinson

Hi Pamela, here's me turning into a Greek puffing up the hill behind the house. There are partridges and woodcock, thrush and quail. There are rabbits. Wild goats. Boar in winter. Scattered on the ground are the first red anemones. Drifts of wood sorrel, white with yellow centres, and chamomile which crushes underfoot as an overweight Greek American walks on it, releasing its scent.

Alethea from across the road's up there most days, collecting chamomile for tea. She's like an American Indian, blacker than a piece of old hide. She lost a hand in an accident. I've never asked how. Alethea's picking chamomile with her good hand, using the blunt stump of her other arm as if it's still got fingers.

Alethea's son Yiannis sometimes comes down the hill with his shotgun and a string of dead birds. Aforementioned partridges, woodcock, thrush, quail. Singing one minute, shot the next. Yiannis is handsome, shorter than me. I remember him from when I was eighteen. Now he's got less teeth. I don't know if he still rides a motorbike.

When Yiannis comes down the hill with his gun he squints his eyes like Clint Eastwood and this overweight Greek American's heart flutters.

Yesterday I came upon him and his mom skinning rabbits. Can life get any more romantic?

*Με αγάπη* (which means 'with love' in Greek) from Chris

## Wonder of wonders

FROM: Pamela Robinson
TO: Chris Woods

Hi Socrates,

Greek life sounds wonderful. Everything here feels ridicu-lously wonderful too—I don't mean to say getting everyone to school on time is easy—or pleasant—but at least everyone is going to school. Raf has a study timetable pinned to the wall of the sleep-out—wonder of wonders. When I declare it's time for the internet to go off, it's turned off without complaint. I wonder what spell Marion put Raf under. We're all being incredibly solicitous of one another—surely it can't last—but for the moment it feels like a blessing.

Remember your crack about Nick not getting any cookies from the jar? Well, believe it or not, he's still hanging around. No turning up unannounced at the flat anymore, thank goodness—there's a moment when continuing to offer to help someone who keeps rebuffing you turns into stalking—but he keeps turning up on my bench at the park at lunchtime. He was there today.

'Don't you ever give up?' I said.

'Nope. I'm attracted to women who don't want me.'

I laughed. 'I bet that's actually true. Before I got married I had a boyfriend who followed me all over the world begging me to marry him. When I finally said yes, he ran away.'

'I don't want to marry you,' he said. 'I don't want to marry anyone.'

We sat in companionable silence, chewing our sandwiches.

'Can I ask what you do want?'

He let out a pantomime cackle and rubbed his hands. 'Wouldn't you like to know? What does anybody want, Pamela? Someone to have dinner with occasionally? Someone to cuddle? I like how expressive your face is. I like how excitable you are.'

'You wouldn't like me full-time,' I said. 'I would drive you nuts.'

'Who said anything about full-time? A regular fuck would be fine.'

We agreed to go to a movie sometime. I haven't told Tünde. With love from the house of peace,

Pamela

X

## Re: Wonder of wonders

FROM: Chris Woods
TO: Pamela Robinson

Hey Socrates, you want to keep living in your house of peace, don't go to the movies with this Nick guy. What did Tünde say about having no room in your life for more emotional engagement? There's a reason you're not telling Tünde about Nick. Am I right? Take care, Chris

## Cookies from the jar

FROM: Pamela Robinson
TO: Chris Woods

Hi Chris,

You're right—as usual—but the reason I don't want to tell Tünde about Nick is because nothing is going to happen. It's not worth discussing. I can't think of anything worse than offering Nick a cookie from the jar—Chris is the only person who has seen me naked in two decades. I'm far too old to sleep with anyone new for a 'first' time. My God—all that appalling who-makes-the-first-move palaver—the appalling morning-after awkwardness.

I no longer remember how to join flesh to flesh anyway—the necessary moves for that seamless assembly. I've forgotten how to kiss. Chris and I were married for thousands of days—breathing the same air night after night, not knowing where our breaths began and ended. Just now, before I got dressed, I stood naked in front of the mirror—a middle-aged woman well on her way to late middle age—not too fat, not too thin—a body which created three living beings. They battered their way out—battering down the doors of my heart on the way. The only proof left that we once lived as one is my sagging stomach. The whole story is there—a pouch left empty; a purse, its brightest coins spent. Who but Chris knows my fallen glories? Who but Mike knows the story written on your skin? Nick Waterman will see only a fallen belly, loose in its pouch.

No way is the cookie jar ever being opened again—the cookie shop is permanently closed.

Love,

Pamela

## Re: Cookies from the jar

FROM: Chris Woods
TO: Pamela Robinson

Hi Pamela, just to be clear: I'm not advising you shut the cookie shop forever. A day might come when you want to risk showing a person your fallen belly. I bet Nick Waterman has a few fallen things of his own. Life's a risk by definition.

I'm risking my butt out on the hill behind the house most days, wrapped in blankets, trying not to get shot. Yiannis is further up the hill blasting the heads off local wildlife. I've got a little chair rigged up, under a juniper tree. No TV up there. No wi-fi. For companionship, there's a skinny brown goat tied to the other side of the tree. The tree's coming into flower. I might brew up some gin when the berries fruit, if I can find out how to make gin.

The air smells of pine needles, oleander, camomile, oregano, and goat. I sit reading on the Kindle I bought with my book voucher, the goat bell knocking. Sometimes I think about the evil twin, wondering if she's forgiven me. A little firecracker like Muaz is going to turn out just fine. Give her food, water, a bed, she does the rest herself. Take care, Chris

## Happy anniversary

FROM: Pamela Robinson
TO: Chris Woods

Hi Socrates,

You know what today is? It's Raphael's seventeenth birthday—but it's also our email anniversary—the day when two women from opposite sides of the earth accidentally began writing down the stories of their lives to send off into space. Chris, you're still a hole in the sky, but you're part of my life now—my lighthouse in the cosmos. Happy anniversary, Chrisanthi Xenia Woods, my invisible friend.

Much love,

Plato

X

## Happy anniversary back

FROM: Chris Woods
TO: Pamela Robinson

Hi Plato, happy anniversary to you too. A whole year. I guess I started writing to you out of curiosity. Then I started wanting to help. Now your emails are like some book I'm reading. When we started emailing I thought nothing interesting was going to happen in my own book. Now I don't know what's going to happen next.

I know some things. I know my mother's going to die one day, in the same room where she was born. Until then, I watch her fighting her fights, singing her same old song. Over here I see her real clear.

I see her bitching about that πατσαβούρα Fotini Chronis, that dirty mop who keeps giving her the evil eye. *Pffft*, does Fotini Chronis have a daughter who is a partner in New York's biggest law firms? Fotini Chronis can't even clean her own house. She's so stupid she pays one of those shifty Albanians to sit in her garden and smoke instead of cleaning. Mom knows about the shifty Albanian because she stands on the veranda with her binoculars, peering into Fotini Chronis's garden.

Mom says: an hour that Albanian's been sitting there smoking.

Who cares? I say back.

What Mom and Fotini Chronis are fighting about is not clear. It's got something to do with Fotini Chronis telling everyone Mom is rich but so mean she refused to give the priest at St Anastasia any money when the church roof fell in. My guess is their fight is left over from some earlier fight. I'm not wasting my time finding out. I just keep thinking my own thoughts, singing my own song.

Happy anniversary, Plato. Take care, Socrates

## Leaving, again

FROM: Pamela Robinson
TO: Chris Woods

Hi again,

How lovely to picture you thinking your own thoughts. You wouldn't believe how often I think of you—wondering how you're going—musing about the texture of your days—wondering if you miss Mike. But honestly, Chris, who among us knows what is going to happen next?

Listen to what happened today in my session with Tünde. I ended up telling her about Nick—I didn't mean to; it just sort of came out. I was talking about how I no longer expected anyone to save me—and that I had lived so long with that buried wish I couldn't recall wishing it in the first place.

'I can't save you either,' she said.

I looked at her, offended. 'I know! That's what I just said!'

She didn't say anything but kept looking at me with a sort of merciless intention.

'I know you can't save me, Tünde. I know no shining prince is going to come knocking on my door.'

She remained silent for a long time before she spoke. 'What's your cemetery-loving Englishman's name? Nick, is it?'

I looked at her crossly. 'Won't his name be in your notes?'

I never thought Tünde could save me! I never thought she was going to issue me with a master plan to follow my whole life long.

'Are you trying to make a point here?' I asked.

Then suddenly it was clear what Tünde was saying—she was telling me in different words that our work was coming to an end. She was telling me I no longer needed her.

She smiled. 'I think you might have forgiven yourself.'

'For leaving?'

She didn't reply.

I was sitting in Tünde's quiet, ordered office—expensive rugs on the floor, pictures of her children on the shelves—and all at once I knew I had the right to leave my marriage, even if my husband did not agree that I should go. The feelings of my heart were mine to claim, and all I had to live on. No-one else—not Chris, not Tünde, not even my children—had the right to claim my feelings—only I did, and I was the one with the responsibility to act on them. I might have been a child whose feelings were dismissed or declared wrong, so that I grew up unable to trust my own judgement, but now I was sitting in my chair, accepting that my feelings were true—and mine.

We sat smiling at each other. When I said goodbye at the door I broke every rule in the book—I leaned over and hugged her. She broke every rule in the book too—she hugged me back.

With love,

Pamela

X

## Re: Leaving, again

FROM: Chris Woods
TO: Pamela Robinson

Hey Plato, your book just keeps getting better. You can only beat yourself up with birch sticks for so long. Now you'll have a regular extra $150 in your pocket. Win-win, right?

Yeah, I'm missing Mike. But right now my old life in Schenectady seems far away. I feel like a girl again, with everything before me. I found an old walking cane in the house. I've started walking.

Yesterday I hauled my butt up the hill, puffing all the way to the top. Behind me, snow is still on the mountains. You can see down into the valley, the road winding to the sea. The days are beginning to get warmer. A few German tourists with backpacks and climbing sticks are starting to arrive, heading for the gorges. The landscape around here is kind of dramatic: cliffs, ravines, hidden lakes in caves. I get why the ancient Greeks spun so many tales from this place: Dionysus was supposed to have stopped by to turn a few folks into trees, the goddess Hera was in these caves, sending virgins mad.

I haven't been down to the hidden lakes in the caves since I was an eighteen-year-old virgin myself. I remember the weird blue light in them, how I couldn't wait to get the hell out. *Με αγάπη*, Socrates

## Hello!

FROM: Pamela Robinson
TO: Chris Woods

Hi Socrates,

I love picturing you puffing up your hill in that wild land-scape—I'm going to surprise you with a visit one day soon, whether you like it or not, using the money I've saved by no longer having to pay for appointments with Tünde. Actually, I haven't stopped seeing her yet—but any day now, I promise. I've realised how hopeless I am at saying goodbye—but now I see my hopelessness for what it is: a refusal to accept that life is fragile and uncertain and that every goodbye holds an intimation of loss. I'm saying goodbye to my losses—soon I'll say goodbye to Tünde too—as I've said goodbye to my marriage, and to my loved brother who left before I was ready—who left before I could say goodbye. I'm saying the farewells I should have said a long time ago and then I'll fly to you across the skies—traversing that cold space where you and I met—where we first said hello. I'm going to keep saying hello—to you—to the world—to life itself. I'm not forgetting I'll have to keep saying goodbye, but I've just remembered the pleasures of hello.

With love,
Pamela
X

### Re: Hello!

FROM: Chris Woods
TO: Pamela Robinson

Hi Pamela, do me a favour and let me know the dates you're planning on coming to say hello. I might drop dead of a heart attack if you turn up unannounced. There'd be no hello then, only one big goodbye.

Here inside the ghost house, nothing but hysterical talk of Easter bread. Which flour makes the best τσουρέκι? Are we going to season it with mastic? What the hell is mastic? (Some sort of resin from a tree.)

I'm staying out of Mom's way. Yesterday, I'm sitting in my chair under the juniper tree when a flock of birds swoops down, the flap of their wings creating this whooshing wind at my back, lifting my hair. I turn around. Nothing but dirt and dust and wind, a giant wind created by crazed birds. Pigeons? Partridges?

Through the dirt I see Yiannis coming down the hill. The sun's behind him. He's lit up. Our eyes meet. He's a dirty, broken-toothed, bird-murdering Greek who has never left the village. He nods. Says hello, asks how I am. Καλά, I say. He keeps walking.

I watch him make his way back down the hill. Sure-footed as a goat. Has he ever been to Athens? Has he ever read a book? I'm looking at Yiannis's back, his stained shirt. Beyond him, the ghost house and inside, Mom going crazy over her τσουρέκι. Take care, Chris

## Chris, again

FROM: Pamela Robinson
TO: Chris Woods

Hi Socrates,

Well, look at you, pining over your bird-murdering Greek—who would have thought it? I promise I'll give you fair warning about coming—I don't mean to come any time soon anyway; this is Raf's big moment—his last year of school—and I wouldn't risk disrupting that.

Other things are occupying my mind at present—Chris is here! Not here at the flat—God forbid—but here in Sydney, staying up the road at a hotel. We've spoken on the phone—arranging where I was going to drop the boys. I invited him for dinner but he said no even before I'd finished asking. He doesn't want to meet me, doesn't want to come for dinner, lunch, coffee or a drink—he made it clear without saying so directly that his preference—still—is never to lay eyes on me.

I couldn't help myself. Even though Chris said he wanted me to drop the boys at the park and leave, I dropped them off and only pretended to drive away. I drove around the corner and parked then snuck back and lurked behind trees. My Chris! Still the same—tall and graceful—easy in his body—fooling around with our sons—letting Baps ride on his back. I watched and watched—filled in equal measure with sadness and hope—realising he was 'my' Chris no longer, but will remain our sons' father forever and ever without end. I stayed watching until they left the park—Raf's silhouette so like Chris's—the same tall grace, the effortless elegant slope of their bodies as they walked away.

I raced back to the car and drove fast to Deb's house, where I sat on her couch and howled. 'What's wrong? For God's sake, what's happened?' she asked.

'Nothing's happened.'

She handed me a box of tissues, looking at me with deep concern.

'Nothing's wrong, Deb. Truly. I just said goodbye.'

'To who?'

I wiped my eyes. 'To my old life.'

She handed me a glass of wine. 'You're an idiot, Pamela Rose Robinson. But you're my idiot.'

We clinked glasses. 'Here's to goodbye,' she said. 'Here's to the past. Farewell.'

Much love from your idiot friend,

Plato

X

## Benevolence

FROM: Chris Woods
TO: Pamela Robinson

Hello, sounds like you're doing fine, Pamela. If I drank I would raise a glass. As I don't, here's me tipping my hat instead: σε εσένα to you!

I told you about the Albanians in town? They're everywhere, doing the crap jobs Greeks don't want. A group of them live outside out of town in an abandoned shepherd's hut. They patched the roof but in winter it must be an icebox. I've seen kids there, with dirty noses and bare feet.

So, the Albanian who sits around smoking in Fotini Chronis's garden instead of cleaning her house starts talking to me in the πλατεία. I'm taking my one coffee of the week, mid-morning at the cafe next to the αρτοποιείο, the bakery. It's where we used to go when I was eighteen to use its communal oven.

The sun's out. I'm entertaining myself reading my future in my upturned coffee cup. The Albanian is suddenly standing in front of me, blocking out the sun. At first I think she's begging.

'Καλημέρα,' she starts.

I'm about to shoo her away.

'You speak English, madam?' she says.

'Sure do,' I say. 'I'm American. I hope I speak English.'

You want the long version or the short one? With or without a side of heartbreak? Her name's Besjana. She's a widow. She's got five kids back in Albania living with her mom. Came to Greece thinking she could send bucket-loads of cash home. Hasn't worked out. She's got tanned skin. Bright blue eyes. Like her eyes wandered off from someone else's face.

She wants more work. Have we got any work at our house?

'You're looking at the woman who does the work in our house,' I say.

She starts crying. I stand up. Start patting her back. I'm thinking, *Jeez, Louise, am I the drop-off point for the world's woes?*

We have got work at our house. Plus a spare bedroom. Warmth, heat, food, a toilet that occasionally flushes. What's a spare bed to a person? In Kalavryta, Mom and I are richer than kings.

I pat Besjana on the back for as long as I can. When she stops crying, I buy her a coffee. I take 20 euros out of my purse.

'Now listen, honey,' I say, 'I can't do any more for you. I can't give you any more money. Please don't ask again. I'll see if anyone's got work. I'll come find you if someone does. I know where you live.'

She nods. She's not crying now. She's drinking her coffee, μέτριος, a little sugar, same way I take it.

'*Merci, merci,*' she says, which immediately makes me doubt her story of crossing the border from Albania into Greece on a dark and stormy night. French, Albanian, Syrian, the world's one big tragic stew. Syrian kids just like Muaz and Zahiya, washing up drowned on Greek beaches. How can I rescue every single one?

I tell Besjana I'd better get back to my mother and her τσουρέκι. I've given everyone what I can. I'm keeping some of God's benevolence for myself. Take care, Chris

## The Fake Grass House

FROM: Pamela Robinson

TO: Chris Woods

Hi Chris,

I'm so pleased you're keeping some of His benevolence for yourself! It's about time. Look at us—the world's tragic stew—me included—all wanting to drink from your cup. Keep it for yourself, Chris—for everything still to come—for Easter and Christmas and all the ordinary days down the track. But promise you'll keep a little bit aside for me when I arrive.

Last night I took the boys out to celebrate Claude passing his first maths exam—and on the way we had an exciting Fake Grass House experience. We were driving past when Claude suddenly shouted, 'Stop! I saw someone!'

'WHAT???' Raf and I said in unison. I slammed on the brakes.

'I saw someone at the Fake Grass House,' said Claude.

'You can't leave us hanging, Claude!' I said. 'Who did you see? Should I turn around?'

He didn't answer. He was next to me, in the front—Raf was sitting with Baps in the back.

'Claude?' I looked across at him—his head was turned away.

'Sweetheart?'

Still he said nothing.

'You big tease,' I said. 'Do you want us to guess?'

I swung the car around. I drove slowly—very slowly—past the Fake Grass House again. Not a curtain parted, not a shutter open, not a door, much less a human face.

'Are you sure you saw someone?'

He nodded. 'I'm sure.'

'What did you see?'

'Something out of the corner of my eye,' he said. 'Something moving.'

We sat in silence, each of us intently watching the Fake Grass House. We sat for a long time. We didn't see anything.

'There's no-one there, Mum,' Raf said.

Still we kept looking. Everything was deathly quiet.

'It's a ghost house,' Raf said.

I smiled. 'I know someone who lives in a ghost house.'

'Really?' said Baps, 'Really, Mum?'

And then I told them about you—Chris on the other side of the world with almost the same name as Dad. I didn't tell them how we met—or that we've yet to meet in person—but I told them you lived in a ghost house in Greece where your mother was born almost ninety years ago, and where her mother lived before that, and her mother before her.

'The same house forever?' said Baps.

'The same house forever. All the people who lived there are ghosts in it.'

No-one spoke. I thought of your ghosts—and mine. I thought of everyone vanished who lives on.

'There's no-one there, Mum,' Raf said again.

I know—I know—but I am not unconsoled—I am not alone—I am not bereft. There's no-one there, but there are shadows glimpsed out of the corner of an eye—there is movement in love's grace—more than anyone can possibly want.

Much love,

Pamela

X

## Spring

FROM: Chris Woods
TO: Pamela Robinson

Γεια σου, Pamela, γεια σου, hello, it's my turn to be glad again. God is good. No shadows at this ghost house. Spring's arrived. Harry's here with his ladders and brushes for whitewashing. Yiannis needs to go down to Diakopto to pick up some fish. He asked if I wanted a ride. Who is going to say no to being eighteen years old again, your hair flying, screaming down a mountain on the back of a motorbike? Με αγάπη, Chris

## The perishing world

FROM: Pamela Robinson
TO: Chris Woods

Oh, Chris—this is our hour—our only moment. This is now, and now, and now—screaming down a mountain on a motor-bike—or howling with loss—sitting quietly in happiness in a car. Knowing every sorrow to come, I would still live my moments. I would live my last moment with Scotty—his loved face in the funeral home—because that moment showed me love. I would choose Christophe Xavier Woods as my husband—I would still run away laughing with him down the street. How else but to live our mistakes—to risk the air of the perishing world? Remember, remember—live it, feel it, cling to it—we are here, we are here, we are here.

Pamela

X

# Flying

FROM: Chris Woods

TO: Pamela Robinson

Hi Pamela, so, here's me, Chris Woods, aged sixty-four, living my moment, holding on to the waist of a man I hardly know, no helmet, my head naked to the world. Here's me, the world reeling, my head thrown back, looking up at the speeding sky. First, I'm looking at balconies, at the astonished faces of Fontini Chronis, Besjana the Albanian, Gregoria from next door and one-handed Alethea from across the road, at the round O of the mouth of Mom's cousin twice removed—and, last of all, at the dumbfounded face of Mrs Calliope Pappas.

*Ελα!* the whole town's crying. *Come! Come see the fat American on the motorbike being driven by Alethea's son, Yiannis!*

*Ωπα!* I shout, my hair flying, speeding past Mrs Katsoulis walking her aged mother back and forth past the washing on their veranda for her afternoon walk. *Ωπα!* I shout at Mom, upstairs on her veranda, scrambling for her binoculars. *Τι θα λεει ο κοσμος?* What will people say?

We're out of town, flying down the hill, the world rushing by, trees, mountains, rivers, houses, the reeling sky. I'm holding on, laughing, I can't stop laughing. I catch a glimpse of Yiannis's face in the mirror. He's staring straight ahead, his Clint Eastwood eyes narrowed as if he's staring down a bad hombre with a gun. I look up, at the sweep of the sky, knowing my bare head could split open like a melon at any moment if I fell off. Do I care? I almost died of happiness. *Με αγάπη*, Chris

## Re: Flying

FROM: Pamela Robinson
TO: Chris Woods

Socrates! How joyous you sound—how alive! I want to see you dying of happiness, before you put the helmet back on. What on earth is going to happen next? Soon you'll be telling me you've taken up smoking.

Plato

X

## How are you?

FROM: Pamela Robinson
TO: Chris Woods

Hi Chris,

Everything OK? Haven't heard from you in a while. Still riding motorbikes down hills with your hair flying?

All good here—nothing to report—which is WONDERFUL.

With love,

Pamela

XXXX

**You there?**

FROM: Pamela Robinson
TO: Chris Woods

Hi Socrates,
　　Now I'm getting worried. What's happening? Are you there?
　　With love,
　　Your friend Plato
　　X

## Earth to Chris

FROM: Pamela Robinson
TO: Chris Woods

Hi Chris,

I don't know why you've disappeared. Did I upset you? Whatever this idiot said to offend you, I'm sorry, sorry and sorry again. *Please* let me know how you are.

You haven't asked how we are, but I'll tell you anyway. We're living our quotidian moments—breaking bread around the table, doing ordinary things like asking each other to pass the salt. We live with the usual complaints—in sadness and happiness—which continues to feel to me like a gift. The boys still squabble. Claude had his phone confiscated at school for using it in class.

I think about you every day—wondering how you are, why you haven't written. Our lives go on—I long to hear how your life is going on too. Please write.

With love,

Pamela

X

# Earth to Chris, Again

FROM: Pamela Robinson
TO: Chris Woods

Chris, are you there? Hello?

## Hello?

FROM: Pamela Robinson
TO: Chris Woods

Hi Chris,

No more Scheherazade of the internet from me. Email when you feel like it. I've given up phoning—your phone just rings out. I've written to Mike in Schenectady—snail mail, weeks ago—no reply. Maybe he didn't even open my letter. He probably thinks it's weird getting a letter from someone he doesn't know—did you tell him about our emails? I tried calling him too—I looked up your number in Schenectady on the internet—but no answer at your home address and no answering message service—the phone rang out. Today is Claude's birthday. Chrisanthi Xenia, love is never absent, just invisible. X

## Thank you

FROM: Pamela Robinson
TO: Chris Woods

If you're there, Socrates, thank you. Thank you for everything—
embodied, or ghostly.
   Much love,
   Plato
   X

## Hello?

FROM: Pamela Robinson
TO: Chris Woods

Hello? Anybody out there? Hello?

## Goodbye story

FROM: Pamela Robinson
TO: Chris Woods

I suppose I am your Scheherazade after all. Here's a story I'm hoping you might like.

Once upon a time there was a woman who was very sad. Her children were sad. Her world was sad. One day she met another woman who arrived in her life as if on a rush of air. The sad woman couldn't see this woman, but she was real, as real as her own sad breath. Over time, because she was helped by this woman, her life changed.

Slowly, slowly, the sad woman's world became less sad, and the sad world of her children became less sad too. They began to live not in a world free of sadness, but in a world of ordinary forgetfulness.

But then a strange thing happened: the woman she could not see disappeared, the invisible disappearing into the invisible, into everywhere and nowhere, into the measureless air on which she had so mercifully arrived.

## Endings

FROM: Pamela Robinson
TO: Chris Woods

The temple bell stops—
But the sound keeps coming
Out of the flowers

Bashō